Stained
By
Blood

A Murder Investigation

Douglas J. Hagmann

Tactical Publications
PO Box 9534
Erie, PA 16505

For more information, please visit: www.StainedbyBlood.com

Stained by Blood

Cover Art by J.D. Hopwood, www.NeptuneDiaries.com

ISBN: 0-9796479-1-6
ISBN-13: 978-0-9796479-1-8

DEDICATION

To my wife, the love of my life.

Prologue

In today's world, perception has become reality. Beliefs become embedded in the average person's perceptions of the world and events around them. But in reality, not all things are as they appear.

I was once told by a man who held a position high in the world of government intelligence that there is an entirely different world of evil and darkness that exists about which the average person knows nothing. That was once my reality and at times, I long to return to the ignorant bliss of that world. You cannot "un-see" what you've already seen, nor can you "un-learn" what you have discovered.

This is my story, as Marc Stiles, of how I came to learn that there are forces of darkness that exist just beyond a very thin veil at the farthest edge of our periphery, that separates good and evil. These forces are real, and the fact that you might not believe it does not disprove their existence. I believe, in fact, that such forces are actually counting on your disbelief so they can continue their deeds unmolested.

Just as forces of evil and darkness exist, so too do does a loving God. You have been given your existence from a loving God for a specific reason, a special purpose in life. In this earthly arena of good and evil, you have a position to play, a job to do. It is up to you to find that purpose through prayer.

As for me, I believe my purpose is to expose the forces of darkness. What you are about to read is the introduction to my earthly task, a task that I have yet to finish.

CHAPTER 1

Wednesday, May 28, 1982

It took me less than five minutes to make the six-mile trip after receiving my father's frantic telephone call. I pulled onto the driveway of my childhood home and was met at the back door by my father. I hadn't seen that look of anguish on his face since having to tell him that I had discovered my mother dead just five years earlier.

I instinctively knew where to go once inside the house, which was the same bedroom where I found my mother. This time, it was my uncle, my father's younger brother. He worked as an elementary school teacher for most of his adult life and had been living with my dad for the last two years. Despite their opposing work schedules, his mere presence seemed to take away some of the emptiness from the house. I could tell my father welcomed the company.

With their opposing schedules, they were able to stay out of each other's way and business, making the living arrangement workable. My father worked third shift as a tool and die maker, while my uncle worked during the day. Uncle Gerald, or 'Jerry' as he was known to everyone, never married, despite his handsome appearance and outgoing personality.

In addition to my father Robert, Uncle Jerry had one older brother and two older sisters, each having a special adoration for him as the youngest of the family and for his various accomplishments in his 52 years on earth.

At first, I stood just inside the doorway of the bedroom, looking at my uncle lying on the blood-soaked bed. Unlike countless deaths I had seen before, I became uncharacteristically frozen at what I saw. The scene immediately assaulted my senses. My uncle's left arm protruded from under a once-white sheet and bedspread with a light floral print. Streaks of now-dried blood dutifully obeyed the law of gravity, streaming down the length of his arm to form a pool of blood that had congealed on the white carpet below his hand. His body was unnaturally wrenched on the bed, his last earthly movements exhibited in a tortured moment forever frozen in time.

I stepped closer to the bed and carefully pulled the bedspread and sheet down. I was hardly prepared for what I saw. My uncle was lying face up on his bed, his left arm extended to the side and over the mattress, and his right arm was unnaturally folded across his chest. There were deep puncture and slashing wounds across both of his forearms. Defensive wounds, I reasoned. A deep slash penetrated his right hand that exposed the bones on each of his fingers, exactly where he grabbed the blade of the knife that was used to kill him. His ashen face was severely contorted, reflecting a combination of pain and fright that would be impossible to describe to anyone who has never seen death in this form.

Having spent the previous five years as a paramedic responding to crime scenes, suicides and unattended deaths of all types, I knew better than to touch or move anything more than I already had. I carefully inspected the bedroom, attempting to make mental notes of what I saw. That was unnecessary, however, as the macabre images were seared into my memory much like those of my mother lying in the same room.

It was also unnecessary as this room was once *my* room, the room where I spent the majority of my childhood until moving out the week after I finished high school.

Memories of a relatively happy childhood spent in the very room where I was standing were quickly and unceremoniously erased. First my mother, and now my uncle. I began to feel lightheaded despite being hardened by my experience as a first responder. The distinctive smell of fresh death permeated the spring air. The room took on the appearance of a slaughterhouse and smelled of gore. Veteran police and emergency workers will tell you that death has its own smell. Particularly, violent death.

Specks and cast-off blood stained the off-white walls and the lampshade on the nightstand as if the killer soaked a rag in blood and spun it up in front of him and over his head. It was like looking at a partially finished Jackson Pollock painting done in shades of mottled red with a bit of Andy Warhol superimposed over the entire bedroom.

As I continued to look around, I caught my reflection in the mirror connected to the top of the dresser. I almost did not recognize myself at that moment, and certainly felt foreign in my childhood room. For a few seconds, the room began to spin, and I felt the coffee I had for breakfast creeping its way to the back of my throat.

I walked to the door where my dad was standing, then walked back to the side of the bed. I recognized the bedspread as being from my father's room. I suddenly remembered that it was the bedspread my mother bought about a month before she died. It was the bedspread that had always been on my dad's bed since she passed away. Now, it was a blood soaked mass of linen that covered the evidence of a frenzied murder.

"Dad, what the hell happened here?"

My father was visibly shaking and choking back tears, "I don't know, Marc. I don't know. This is the way I found him when I got home from work," he said, finally breaking down. "I called you first and then called for an ambulance."

Almost like a genie summoned by its master, Russ, the chief paramedic of the rescue unit where I was assigned until about a month before, abruptly appeared and brushed past my dad, suddenly reappearing on the opposite side of the bed. Russ and I had known each other for several years and worked together for four. He took one look, raised his eyes to meet mine and simply shook his head, delivering the news we already knew in a manner I had seen so many times in the past. He escorted my dad to the dining room, sitting him down at the table where the entire family had dinner the previous evening. I could hear him using the familiar radio codes to summon the coroner and the police, after which he sent his partner Tim, who wandered into the bedroom for a look and back to the dining room, back to the rig.

Russ called me into the dining room to join my father, but I did not immediately respond. I wanted to take one last look around the bedroom and one last look at the unspeakable carnage done to my uncle before the police arrived. For some inexplicable reason, I felt I had to mentally document as much as possible. I prepared myself and tried desperately to detach myself from the reality that it was my uncle who was lying dead in front of me.

I took one more look at my uncle's twisted face, his lifeless eyes open in a dazed stare and mouth open like a silent scream in the dark of night. I was trying to imagine what it was he last saw. Who it was. I tried counting the number of stab wounds on his body, in his chest, stomach, shoulders and arms. Fifty, I thought. No, maybe twenty. I don't know. There was a deep slash across his throat, leaving a gaping wound that revealed a portion of his windpipe and one carotid artery. The cut extended so deeply that I could almost make out a portion of his spine. I lifted the sheet and blanket a bit more, noting that the stab wounds appeared to be limited to his upper body. One wound penetrated his abdomen just below his sternum. That stab wound seemed to be made at such an angle that it tore open his skin, exposing a portion of his intestines.

I placed the sheet and comforter back over his body, trying to match the stains on the material to the pattern on his body.

What kind of sick bastard could commit such a gruesome murder? Carefully replacing the bedspread and trying to mentally process what I saw, I walked from the room to the dining room table to be with my dad.

Before reaching the dining room, something caught my attention in the bathroom located just outside of my uncle's bedroom, across the hallway. It was a bloody bath towel lying on the floor near the combination bath and shower. I heard myself whispering, "What the hell..."

The morning sun shining through the uncovered window revealed an unexpected, sickly scene. In addition to the blood-stained towel, the walls of the shower stall were blood stained, and a bar of soap was streaked in blood. A soapy mix of dried blood and water streaked from the bar of soap toward the bathtub. A near-perfect palm print, with five fingers extending outward was clearly visible on the wall of the shower stall. Looking closer, I saw a mixture of blood, water and soap pooled by the drain.

The sick son of a bitch not only butchered my uncle, but stuck around to shower afterward. The room began spinning again, and I desperately fought to detach myself from the horror that occurred hours before.

My thoughts were interrupted by Russ, who now *ordered* me to the dining room table. "Marc, get in here. You know better," he said rather sternly, not wanting me to disturb the crime scene. I entered the dining room and sat at the table next to my dad.

In preparation for the police, Russ used his radio to obtain the times of the call, dispatch and arrival, writing each down on a separate line on the notepad he removed from his jacket. He then turned his attention to my father, asking him the normal questions of a first responder. It was clear that it would be all business from here.

Seconds later, a uniformed officer arrived, followed by a second officer. Minutes later, we were ushered from the house by a detective, and watched helplessly as the police unrolled the crime scene tape across the exterior of the house. My next memory was being in the back of a marked police car parked in front of my former home, seated next to my father. Inside, I heard the faint but familiar clicking noise made by the emergency light bar on top of the marked unit. My mind raced over the details of the frenzied scene I just saw, like someone suddenly awakened from an all-too-real nightmare.

My stream of consciousness was jolted by a voice coming from the front of the car. It was Sergeant Ron Jenkins of the Lakewood Police Department, telling us that he was taking us to the police station until they "sorted things out."

Being a first responder in a relatively small city, I knew most of the cops, including Ron. He spent the last ten years as a patrol officer, and rose to the rank of supervisor two years ago. He was ready to move up to the detective division. We last saw each other the week before as we shared a pitcher of beer and an order of chicken wings at Rossi's Tavern. He beat me in a game of pool, something that obligated me to pay for the second pitcher. Russ and several other cops and paramedics were also at Rossi's that night, a quiet haunt that gave cops and first responders a place to unwind and vent.

As we pulled away from the house, we passed a news crew van heading towards my former home. My dad twisted his neck around to follow the van. Jenkins told my father not to worry, that the detectives would handle them. He then asked me if my pool game improved any in the past week, trying to be as casual as possible for a time like this.

For my dad's sake, I tried to remain detached and told Jenkins that I would beat him the next time, while numerous disjointed thoughts continued to spin uncontrollably in my head. Inexplicably, I was glad that we were not in handcuffs. But then, why should we be? At that moment, I looked down and noticed that there was blood on my right forearm. My mind raced and whirled at the sight of the blood, wondering if I had somehow cut myself. It's funny how a person's mind works in situations like this. Checking out my hands and arms carefully, it was then I realized that it was a transfer stain. I must have brushed up against something in the bedroom. I looked up and caught Ron looking at me through the rear view mirror. He quickly averted his gaze back to the street.

"Ron, I've got some blood on my arm," I said. "Yeah, I saw it," he replied, not taking his eyes off the road. After several seconds of uncomfortable silence, he said that they would take care of it at the station. My father sat in frozen silence next to me, saying nothing as we proceeded to the police station.

A few more minutes of uncomfortable silence went by, broken by my dad asking Jenkins if we were under arrest. "No, not at all," he said. "We just need to take your statements and get your prints."

"Why do you need *our* fingerprints?" asked my dad.

"Elimination prints, so we have them on file to rule you guys out," stated Jenkins.

It was at that point that my father realized that he was a suspect and, because of his call to me, I was also a suspect. My dad began to protest, telling Jenkins that he called me to come over and I got there only a few minutes before they did.

"Relax, Bob," he said. "It's just routine. Anyway, I know Marc and I feel like I know you, too. I'm sure you'll be in and out in no time at all."

We arrived at the Lakewood Municipal Building that housed the police station. We were immediately escorted by two uniformed officers from the back of the car into two different interview rooms. We were questioned separately by two detectives. Three or four Polaroid photographs of the blood on my arm were taken, and I was allowed to wash up, only to have my fingers and palms stained by the ink from the fingerprint rollers. On my second trip to the wash room, I met my dad who was also washing the ink from his hands.

"You doing okay?" I asked him.

"Did you know about Jerry, what he was? His 'other' life? Or am I the *only* idiot in the whole damn family?" asked my dad. His demeanor struck me as odd. His angst now seemed to morph into a generalized anger—a type of deep, disturbing anger I had only seen a few times since my early childhood. I knew I was standing on thin ice, and I was searching for the right thing to say.

I had my deep suspicions about my uncle since high school, but never brought up the subject with my father. After all, decent people don't talk about such things At least that was my reasoning. Anyway, I really thought he knew about his brother's 'other' life. He had a hell of a lot longer time on earth with him then I did, and he was living with him for Pete's sake. Was he being intentionally naive or did he really not know?

"Dad, I—"

"You *what*? What, Marc? You couldn't come to me, you couldn't talk to me?" His imposing frame was inching closer to me. Even through his bleary eyes, his stare easily burrowed into my brain. I didn't know what to say. So, I took the easiest way out that I could think of at that moment.

"Dad, I didn't know, at least not for sure. You know I wasn't that close to him."

He stopped less than a foot away from me, now positioned well within my comfort zone. He stared at me for what seemed like an eternity, sizing me up for any indication of dishonesty. I stood absolutely still, staring back in abject defiance. Finally, he turned and used the paper towel he was holding to wipe the moisture from his eyes.

"Dad, I'm sorry."

"So am I, Marc."

We left the wash room at the same time, and this time were escorted to a single interview room already occupied by the two plain clothes detectives who previously interviewed us individually.

I looked at my watch. It was 11:23 a.m. Three hours had gone by quickly, yet time seemed to stand still. My head pounded and my stomach ached. Jenkins popped his head into the room and asked us if we wanted anything to drink.

"Coffee" was the response from both me and my dad, saying it in near stereo.

"Thought you would," he said, and magically produced two cups in a cardboard tray from McDonald's, which he had been shielding by the wall. "There's cream and sugar there too, if you want it," he said, closing the door after placing the tray on the table in front of us.

Detective Michael 'Mack' McCarty entered the room where we were now both sitting, taking a seat opposite both of us. Placing a legal sized brown folder on the table in front of him, he opened the folder and crushed the stubby remains of a Pall Mall into the plastic ashtray next to him.

"I'm the lead detective on this case," McCarty blurted. "Go ahead, drink your coffee. We're just about done here," he said, brushing his mustache with one hand while looking through a folder of notes in front of him. As we drank our coffee, the mood seemed to relax a bit, although it was still all business.

McCarty broke the silence. "We've got several good sets of prints from the scene belonging to three different people. Only one that appears to be a suspect, though, and none were a match to either of you." Looking at my father, he said, "We also checked on your work schedule and confirmed that you never left work the entire night."

Turning his head to me, he said "We've established where you were, too. Now this is just preliminary, but the coroner put the time of death at 2:00 a.m., 'give or take'. Considering the evidence from the scene, and what we already have, we don't consider either of you suspects. But for the time being, you'll both need to stick around in case we need to ask you more questions. And I'm sure we'll have plenty, so don't be planning any exotic European vacations," McCarty said with the hint of a smile. "Unless you let us know in advance."

Still visibly shaken, my father combined questions and statements and fired them in rapid succession at McCarty, without giving him any time to answer. "What happened? You've got to know what happened. Who would do this? Nobody I know would ever want to hurt Jerry and certainly not kill him. He's a great guy and everybody loves him." Seeming to tire quickly, my dad's voice trailed off and he began to sob. I simply hung my head. I was never good at comforting my dad, not even when my mom died.

I just wanted to go home, back to the home of my childhood, back in time, back to recapture innocence lost. I wanted my mother now more than ever. I felt guilty that I could not comfort my dad. I felt guilty that I could not remember the last time I told my mother I loved her before finding her lifeless body, taken from me by a sudden heart attack while she slept. I just felt guilty about my feelings, while my heart ached for my father.

"Alright, you two can go," said McCarty, who assured my dad that they would find out what happened and who killed his brother.

"Go where?" My dad's question seemed to linger in the air. He had been at his job all night and could not go back to the home he knew, as detectives were still processing the scene. I was so immersed in my own concerns that, sadly, I never thought about that.

"Your other brother, Keith, is here to take you to his house, at least until we can let you go back to your own."

"He knows what happened to Jerry?" asked my dad. "Yes, we told him, of course. He wants you to stay with him and Sherrie until we finish at your house. Go ahead, go with him," said McCarty in a compassionate tone.

I saw Uncle Keith put his arm around my father, and they both walked out of the room and the station-house. Still sitting at the interview table, McCarty lit up another Pall Mall and asked me if I needed a ride anywhere. "Yeah, I gotta go back to get my car. It's at my, err— my dad's house," I replied. "Fair enough. Jenkins will take you back up there."

McCarty leaned forward and looked into the hallway. He motioned for Jenkins, who then walked into the room. "Listen Marc, we'll get the guy who did this, don't worry. I wouldn't be surprised if we wrapped this up in 24 hours. Two or three days, tops." He then told Jenkins to take me back to "the crime scene," where my car was parked. I cringed at hearing my childhood home being called a crime scene.

For the second time that morning, I found myself in the back seat of a police car. When we stopped at a red light, I looked out the rear door window of the police cruiser at a station wagon being driven by a middle-aged woman with a younger child in the front passenger seat. The child was pointing me out to his mother, who turned her gaze in my direction. "I guess he thinks I'm a 'perp,'" I said quietly, to no one in particular.

Jenkins was more talkative on this trip than he was before. "Man, I'm really sorry for you guys. This really sucks. I really feel bad for your uncle. Looks like he put up quite a struggle from what I understand. I'm really sorry, Marc. If there is anything I can do—" I cut him off mid-sentence.

"No, there's nothing. Just make sure you guys find the bastard who did this, OK?"

"You know 'Mack' is the best. He'll find the scumbag. Whoever did this will pay," said Jenkins. As he dropped me off in front of my old childhood home, I looked beyond the police tape, the marked and unmarked police cars, and the press gathering.

"It doesn't look the same, Ron," I said.

"What do you mean, Marc? What, is something missing?" he asked, wondering if I saw something amiss that would help the police.

"Ron, remember the old saying that you can't go home again? It's gone, Ron. My home is gone." I felt a deep and sudden sadness wash over me. My sadness was quickly replaced by anger and rage at whoever did this. Whoever killed my uncle. Whoever hurt my dad. Whoever stole my memories.

With that, I shut the door to the police car that Ron had opened from the outside, and I stepped onto the grass that was once the yard where I played with my childhood friends. Even the grass looked and felt different. *I* felt different.

Before he could leave, a news crew from one of the local stations put a microphone in my face, blurting out questions that I didn't hear or care to answer. Mercifully, Ron moved them back and away from me, asking them to give me some privacy.

As I quickly drove away, I looked in my rear view mirror. I expected to see my former home. Instead, I saw innocence lost amid the unmarked police cars and the stable of media reporting from the front of the house.

CHAPTER 2

Tuesday, April 28, 1987

I woke up with a raging hangover, the result of a night of drinking straight bourbon at Rossi's Tavern. My bedside alarm was blaring, or so it seemed, cutting a merciless path into the deep recesses of my brain like a dull knife. I shut off the alarm and sat on the edge of my bed, trying to get my bearings. The bitter aftertaste of whiskey and cigarettes made me nauseous, as it had done countless times in the recent past. Last night, I had more than my share of both.

As I tried to shake off the lingering effects of Jim Beam, my mind began to race. I lit a Marlboro as I walked to the coffee maker following a brief stop at the bathroom. It was five years ago today, I thought, astonished at how quickly time had passed. So much has changed over the last five years, except for one thing. The man who killed my uncle and shattered my family is still out there. I began to replay the events of that day in 1982, remembering it like it was yesterday.

I stood at the sink, impatiently watching the coffee maker slowly dispense its magical nectar into the glass pot. Unwilling to wait the extra few minutes, I grabbed a ceramic cup from the counter and slipped it underneath the stream of steaming hot liquid, moving the coffee pot away to accommodate the cup and my immediate need for caffeine.

I stood at the counter and downed my first cup of coffee black, not having the energy to make the short walk to the refrigerator for cream. Reaching next to the coffee maker, I turned on the radio to the local FM rock station. Dexy's Midnight Runners *Come on Eileen* was streaming from the one working speaker of the radio.

Wow, I thought, as that was the same song that was playing on my car stereo as I raced to meet my father exactly five years ago today. Like a familiar song often does, it transported me back in time to that day and back into my car. Memories of that day flooded back to me quicker and with more clarity than the events of last night.

Still struggling with my senses of the present, I looked at my watch. It was 8:07 a.m., and I had to get to my office by nine. I have a long day of work ahead of me, I thought. I refilled my empty cup with more coffee, and carried it into the bathroom, where I turned on the shower. As the water struck my face, I slowly regained my faculties that I had deliberately dulled the previous night. The water hitting my body was as hot as I could stand it, and the force of the stream was nearly pinning me against the shower wall, compliments of my indulgences.

As I stood in the shower, I began to make a mental recap of the last five years of my life. Having just turned 28 a week earlier, I was already married and divorced, with two small children. I changed professions from that of a paramedic to a private detective, with a few career changes nestled in-between.

Shortly after my uncle's murder, I decided that I had my fill of responding to emergency calls, extricating people from gnarled cars or carrying them down multiple flights of stairs. I had all I could take of the senseless deaths of infants and children, people at their prime, and those of all ages, by causes ranging from the most horrendous to the more 'routine.' Although I was only 23 at that time, I had grown tired of the death, the heartache, and the dangers.

I had enough of running into burning buildings as people were running out, and I had seen enough pain and sadness to last me a lifetime. I stopped counting the fatalities I had seen at three hundred, a number I reached only 18 months into my career as a paramedic and firefighter. I simply had enough.

I had gotten my private investigator badge just four months ago. My ID card was dated January 5, 1987, the same day that I became a partner with Paul Owen, the owner of a small private investigation company located in Lakewood. Paul is a cowboy, the type of private detective of books and movies. Even though he is not well liked by the local district attorney, I like him, and we get along well.

I continued my mental journey, recalling how my divorce and numerous other personal and professional choices had caused an estrangement between me and my father, who himself remarried during the last five years to a long-time family friend. Being an only child has its good aspects and bad, but I felt like it had been all bad for the last five years. No, I thought, it's been bad for the last decade.

I was jarred back to the present as the water quickly turned from hot to cold. A bit more awake now, I somehow found myself agreeing with my father's sad assessment of my life. Aside from my two young children, though, I began thinking about the one 'hopeful' treasure amid all of the pain and heartache. Her name is Deana Griffiths, a bright and beautiful woman of Welsh lineage I met a few years back while working at a temporary career layover in my journey to becoming a private detective.

Deana is the mother of one boy who was born the same year as my youngest daughter. From the moment I met her, I knew that we were meant to be soul mates. We had recently become reacquainted when I stopped at the insurance company where she works. While talking to her during my visit last January, I asked if she would like to join me for lunch. She did, and we began having lunch together a couple of times a week.

Then, I asked her one day to join me for drinks after work, and she did. That night, I poured my heart out to her, telling her everything that was going on in my life— the good, the bad, and the ugly.

I felt that we made a deep connection that night, but there was just one problem. She had just gone through a difficult divorce and made it clear that she was not interested in becoming involved with anyone, or starting any new relationships. I continued talking with her was when she was at work, although that was limited to the constraints of her job. We still had our lunches, whenever possible, although they seemed to be more infrequent as her personal stresses grew.

It was almost nine o'clock when I left my apartment for the office. Still nursing my hangover, I drove through McDonald's for an extra-large cup of black coffee. The aroma of the coffee permeated my car and brought my dulled senses back to life. I grabbed the coffee, my briefcase filled with file folders of current cases, and walked into my office ten minutes later than my usual time of arrival.

Annie Knoll, the secretary Paul hired in mid-January, was already at her desk and hard at work, typing a surveillance report on the new electric Smith Corona typewriter we purchased two weeks ago. She had complained that we needed to "get into the 80's" by replacing the old Royal manual typewriter that possessed a temperamental space bar with something more modern. She smiled and greeted me with a cheerful "Good morning" as I unlocked the inner door to my personal office. I managed a mere grunt in return.

I placed my briefcase on top of my desk and walked back to the doorway to my office. "I'll be busy writing a report for the next few hours, so please hold all my calls," I said to Annie, who looked up as I came into her view.

"Do you really want me to hold all of your calls, Marc?" she asked with a wry smile, adding an extra punch to the words "really" and "all."

"Okay, you know the only one I'll take, Annie." I managed to force a smile and shut my door, realizing that she knew that the only person I wanted to talk to was Deana.

"You've got it bad, Marc. I can tell love, and you're in it," Annie said through the closed door.

I walked back to my desk and opened my briefcase, moving my .38 Smith & Wesson revolver to the top right-hand drawer of my desk. On top of all of the other active cases I was working, the top file folder labeled I-163 would remain the focus of my attention for the rest of the day. I-163 was the number assigned to the unsolved homicide of Gerald 'Jerry' Stiles. I grabbed the file and my coffee, and sat down in my faux leather desk chair. Lighting up another Marlboro, I sat there for the next hour, pouring over all of the notes and reports pertaining to the murder of my uncle.

Oh, the irony, I thought. Five years to the day, and now I'm holding the file of my uncle's unsolved murder. A murder that was supposed to take only "a day or two, tops" to solve, at least by the assurances of Lakewood's finest. Now, the file was in my hands.

It was shortly after I had become Paul's partner that my dad called me unexpectedly, and reluctantly asked me to talk with Paul about the murder. "Maybe we need his involvement into the case, as we've gotten nowhere with the Lakewood Police. It's a cold case, they said. So, ask Paul and I'll have your aunts and uncle here so Paul can meet them. They'll tell him what they know, and maybe Paul can work the case. You are welcome to come too," my dad said.

"Gee, thanks, dad, I really appreciate the offer," I responded during this short telephone conversation.

The date of the call was in the folder notes. It was January 19th, 1987. I really didn't need to look at the notes to remember the pain and sadness that call generated, or to remind me of our estrangement. I talked with Paul later that day, and he agreed to look at the case, and reassured me that we were a team, regardless of my dad's feelings toward me. Paul called my father later that evening.

The following week, on Sunday, January 25, 1987, I accompanied Paul to meet with my father and his surviving brother and two sisters at the house he shared with his wife Jeanne, my stepmother. It was an uncomfortable meeting, although a productive one. By a unanimous agreement among family members, we got the case. Paul offered to take the case for expenses only, plus $1.00 for our time, a bureaucratic necessity to comply with the licensing standards set forth by the State of Ohio.

As the executor of Uncle Jerry's estate and the point of contact with the police, my dad signed the contract that permitted us to work the case on behalf of the family. He also signed several blank standard release forms for whatever documentation we needed relative to Uncle Jerry's life and death.

As we left the house later that evening and walked to his car, Paul handed me the dollar and told me to buy myself a cup of coffee. I crumpled the dollar bill and tossed it inside the open door of my dad's garage.

Later that night, I spent a few hours thinking about the case over bourbon and water supplied to me by Brenda, the cute, young, blond-haired bartender at the Towne Bar, an upscale bar and restaurant located about a half-mile from my apartment. I attempted to mitigate whatever feelings of rejection I felt earlier that day with my favorite elixir, a pack of Marlboros, and Brenda's tolerant ear. I was a 'regular' there, and Brenda knew me well.

Recalling the events of that cold and wet day last January, I experienced another wave of nausea, although I was uncertain whether it was from my activities the previous night or just thinking about that family meeting. Just then, I heard a quiet knock on my office door.

"Come in," I said, just over a whisper. The door opened and Annie appeared, carrying a paper cup filled halfway with water from the office water cooler and a mercy dose of Alka-Seltzer, which she had been carrying around in her purse for just such an occasion. "I thought you could use this," she said, as she placed the cup and packet of hangover reliever on the corner of my desk.

"How did you know?" I asked, looking up from the thick folder. "Have you looked in a mirror this morning? It doesn't take a detective to see that you had a rough night," she said, with that familiar smile she formed with her lips.

Annie, just 25 years old, was proving to be the glue that seemed to hold the office together. She knew more about me, Paul, and most of the cases than she would ever tell, and she kept things running smoothly between me, Paul, and three other investigators who worked for us full time. An attractive and mature 25, she is unmarried, uninvolved at the moment, and clearly focused on her job. She is self-motivated with a penchant for solving mysteries, traits that fit well with this line of work.

"So, where is everybody this morning?" I asked, hoping to maintain the tranquility of a quiet office for at least the rest of the morning.

"Well, Paul is meeting a client to negotiate a security contract. Gary and Gina are on a surveillance for Nabb's Trucking, and Richard won't be in until this afternoon. So, it's just you and me this morning, I guess. Nothing else is on the schedule, but Paul wants to talk with you later, sometime after lunch," explained Annie.

She then asked if I had any plans for lunch, which was her way of finding out how my pursuit of Deana was going. She was well aware of her situation, and understood, perhaps better than I did, the pursuit of someone who removed herself from the relationship pool.

"I don't know yet," I said, hoping that Annie might offer a word of encouragement. "She'll call, and if she doesn't, I can get her on the phone for you if you'd like," she said, adding, "You've got to get things handled. I hope you know that she's a once-in-a-lifetime catch. You need the stability. You can't go back to chasing anything in a skirt with a pulse. And you certainly can't come into the office looking like you do this morning," she said in a protective fashion.

"I know, Annie. I know," I said. As she walked out of my office, I called out to her. She paused at the doorway as she turned around to look at me. "Thanks." It was all I could say at that moment. She gave me a quick smile, then continued to the outer office, quietly shutting my door as she left.

I opened the pack of Alka-Seltzer, dropping the wafers into the water, and drank the fizzing mix in two large gulps. Crumpling the paper cup, I threw it into the corner wastebasket after bouncing it off the two adjacent walls. I walked to a 4' x 6' cork board hanging on the side wall of my office, looking over the rows and columns of index cards I created of all of the people in my uncle's life. Everybody was a suspect. No one was a suspect. No fingerprint matches.

I adjusted the strands of yarn connecting the index cards to one another. The types of connections were denoted by yarn color, and the index cards contained all of the relevant biographical data—including the current contact information of all those who were potentially involved. Two hours passed quickly.

"Pretty soon I'm going to need a bigger board," I said out loud to exercise my voice.

As the investigation progressed, more people were being identified. "And more index cards," came a voice from the door of my office. It was Annie, who opened the door to tell me that Mary Clayburn, the crime reporter for the Lakewood Daily Press, was on the telephone, requesting to talk with me.

"I know it's not the call you were expecting, but I think you should talk to her," Annie said. "I think she knows about your uncle's other life, and it sounds like she might run with a story about it," added Annie.

"Thanks, I'll take it." A bit agitated that Mary was interrupting my flow of thought, and that it was not the person I really wanted to talk to, I pushed the button for line one and picked up the receiver.

"Marc, I want you to know that I'm not your enemy. I'm just doing my job." Those were the words of Mary Clayburn before I even had the chance to say anything but "Hello."

"For not being my enemy, you sure as hell are causing me a boatload of grief," I replied back.

"Let's talk. How about tonight at your office, say, six o'clock," Mary pressed.

I reluctantly agreed, adding that Paul would have to be part of the meeting, knowing that he would agree as well. After hanging up, I leaned out my door and asked Annie to confirm the Clayburn meeting with Paul when he called in for his messages. It's going to be another long day, I thought.

Paul never did stop at the office after lunch, and both Gary and Gina went home after their assignments. Richard was sick and stayed home, so it was just me and Annie for the rest of the day. Deana never called, and I was in a full, post-hangover, depressed mode.

I stayed inside my office through 5:30 p.m., reviewing notes and rearranging cards on the board, except for the occasional bathroom breaks.

Shortly after 5:00, Annie knocked on my office door and opened it after I told her to come in.

"Unless you need me for anything else, I'm going home now. I put the phones over to the answering service, and finished the Phillips and Zelnick surveillance reports. Do me a favor, Marc," said Annie.

"What's that?"

"Print for goodness sakes. Or use the cassette player for dictation. I can barely read your writing!"

"Good night, Annie. I'll see you in the morning."

"See ya, and oh, good luck with Mary tonight." I grumbled a bit as she closed the door as she left. I reached for another cigarette, only to find the pack empty.

I got up, put on a half-pot of coffee and walked to the lobby of our office building. I fed seven quarters into the coin slot and pulled the handle for Marlboro, noting that it was the last pack in the machine. As it fell into the open slot below the glass front of the machine, Paul walked in.

"You gotta stop that, Marc. It's gonna kill you some day, and your money is going up in smoke," he said in a scolding manner. "Come on, let's talk before Mary gets here. We have to be on the same page."

For the next 15 minutes, Paul and I went over the progress of file I-163, otherwise known as the Stiles murder investigation. That has an odd ring to it, I thought. Murder combined with one's own last name.

Paul said that we would not reveal anything to the reporter beyond what she already knows, except that we are looking at one or two people very closely as potential suspects. I asked about how he wanted to handle my uncle's other life, if it should come up.

"It's not going to come up, Marc. I won't let it. Not now. The cops don't want it confirmed, either," Paul said.

"Paul, I think Mary knows," I said. "I think that's why she's coming over, to talk about breaking this as a development on the case."

The next few sentences from Paul were expletive-filled characterizations of the press in general. He assured me that he would manage the flow of information from our office. Just then, Mary Clayburn walked through the door.

"I heard that, Paul" Mary said.

"Good. Then we both have a starting point for this meeting. Now, what can we do for you?" Paul sat back in his chair, putting his feet up on the desk, revealing his gray and black snake skin cowboy boots. "Have a seat."

Mary walked to a chair in front of Paul's desk, just to my left. She looked over at me and said, "You look like hell. What did you do, pull an all-nighter?" I ignored her and looked at Paul to relieve me from her unsolicited assessments.

After a long pause where nobody seemed to blink or inhale, Mary said that she wanted to see if we would be interested in being profiled in a local, human interest story about our P.I. business, considering the popularity of the hit television series Moonlighting starring Bruce Willis and Cybill Shepherd. Mary suggested that Gina, our female investigator, could be compared to Maddie Hayes, and either Paul or I to Willis' character David Addison.

"Mary, please tell me you're not serious," pleaded Paul. Mary began to laugh, and said that her editor really did want her to at least bring it up as a human interest story to be done by another reporter who writes for the Lifestyle section of the Lakewood Daily News. Paul relented for the sake of good will. "Tell your editor to call me later in the week and we'll set something up," assured Paul. "But tell us what you're really here for, Mary."

Mary's expression turned dark and foreboding. Looking directly at me, she told me that she knew what the family was trying to hide about my uncle. She said that she knew how bad it would look that my uncle, the school teacher and former principal of an elementary school, was a homosexual. She suggested that his sexual proclivities were a possible motive for his murder, something we had obviously considered since the first minute we took the case.

"I've been hearing things out there. Lakewood is a pretty small town despite its size. I think you might be making some people nervous. You know," said Mary, "skeletons don't like to live in closets."

"First off, Mary, my father did not even know until the police told him the day he found him dead. Sure, there was suspicion, but he kept his two lifestyles separate. It's not like anyone was trying to hide anything, especially my family. But because it could possibly go to motive for his killing, it's something we wanted to keep under wraps only for that reason. If you run with this, frankly, I think you'll get more grief from the police than us," I said.

Mary asked if I would confirm his homosexual lifestyle on the record.

"Not from me, not from us, Mary," was my response. "And if you want to help us, and if you want any further exclusives from our investigation, you'll withhold this bit of information for a little while longer.

"And, just for the record, like you said, there are some very prominent and powerful people in Lakewood who could be involved in—"

"Marc, that's enough!" Paul interrupted and scolded me in just three words. He glared at me from above his glasses that rested on the lower part of his nose. I immediately shut up.

Paul deflected my statement by telling Mary that we're looking at a person of interest in the state of Florida as a potential suspect. Mary asked if she could go on record with that piece of news. Paul agreed that she could.

Mary asked us if we already talked to the Florida suspect. Paul told her no, but said that I was going to be going down to interview the suspect in a few weeks. That's news to me, I thought, although I did not openly express my surprise.

After a half-hour of conversation, Mary Clayburn said that she had enough for an updated news story to satisfy her editor and that she would notify us before it hit the paper. As she left, she wished us luck. With both of us still seated, Paul and I picked up where we left off before her arrival, rehashing the progress of the case.

"Five years today, my friend," he said. "We're going to solve this case, no matter what. I don't give a damn what it takes. We're going to show the police how it's done." Moving his boot-clad feet from his desk, he opened a desk drawer and tossed a shoulder holster on my lap.

"That's for you. Wear it," he said. "Don't go anywhere without your gun on you. Get it out of your briefcase. Keep it on you. You'll never know who or what could be waiting for you. I've got a feeling we're going to be hitting some nerves with some very prominent people."

I had no idea how true his words of caution would prove to be.

Exhausted, I left the office and drove straight back to my apartment. My thoughts were consumed by Deana, and I wondered what she was doing at this very moment. I walked into my apartment, tossed my keys on the kitchen counter, and checked my answering machine for messages.

Before I even pressed the button, I could tell there were no new messages. The light was solid red. But I played through my old messages just to hear Deana's voice from a message she left several days before. It was soothing, and made me want her even more. But I knew that I could not be too pushy, as I might end up pushing her away. I looked at the clock on the wall. It was just after 8:00 p.m.

Flopping down on the blue couch lent to me by my landlord, I turned the television on to a rerun of *MacGyver* and fell asleep within minutes. I was still wearing my sport coat and tie, not having the energy to change. The trials of the day drifted away just as MacGyver was creating some type of life-saving device out of bubble gum and duct tape. If it was only that easy.

CHAPTER 3

Thursday, April 30, 1987

I awoke to the sound of my alarm just after 6:00 a.m., anxious to begin my day. Today is the day that Paul Owen, Gina Russell and I are to conduct a full review of my uncle's murder case from top to bottom, start to finish. Paul decided to bring Gina into the investigation for a fresh set of eyes, and to cover for him as he is spending a lot more of his time trying to start a security company as an offshoot of the investigative agency.

We are planning a painstaking review all of the facts pertaining to the murder, including a full review of everything we had done to advance the investigation from the day we accepted the assignment to the present. We set aside all other cases and already requested that Annie make arrangements for a steady supply of coffee to be furnished to us and lunch ordered in. She will also act as a gatekeeper so we would not be disturbed by phone calls and other distractions. The meeting was scheduled to begin at 10:00 a.m. and last the entire day, or until we were finished going over every aspect of the case.

Although the murder case continued to occupy my thoughts over the last few days, I was unable to devote any time to my own personal field investigation of the murder.

I spent Tuesday and Wednesday working on a claim for Aetna Insurance Company. A man filed a claim for the loss of his brand new Cadillac that he said someone stole from his driveway two weeks prior. Of course, the man claimed to have left a box of his wife's jewelry inside the car, as he was planning to take the valuables to the jewelry store for cleaning and minor adjustments. The total value of the missing jewelry actually exceeded the value of the car, which made the claims adjuster very suspicious. After two days of investigation and interviews, I was very suspicious as well.

The claimant is no ordinary client of Aetna. He is an established client with no previous claim history. More importantly, he is a federal court judge, a man appointed to his position by the president of the United States. I had already taken his recorded statement and procured the police report. I also obtained all of the appraisals of the jewelry that were on file with the insurance company, and interviewed the jewelry store owner, the man's neighbors and close friends. All of the information lined up nicely, which always sends up red flags in my view. Too tidy, and I don't like tidy when it involves these types of incidents. It suggests that the incident was staged and the witnesses were prepped, as if they were reading from a prepared script. Late last night, I set that file aside for a closer review. I wanted to go over my findings with Gina, who seemed to have a special talent in punching holes in people's stories.

Yesterday, I was fortunate enough to have an extended lunch with Deana between interviews. She looked radiant when we met at a local upscale restaurant in Lakewood. We spent over an hour talking about all sorts of things, yet nothing in particular. It was just an opportunity to spend some precious time with her.

After our lunch, we hugged as we said our good-byes. For the rest of the day, I could smell the light scent of her perfume on my suit coat. Every once in a while, I would get a whiff of the scent from my coat, and it would take me back to our time together and remind me of her beauty. Totally smitten, I dreamed of our future together. It seemed so far off that it felt unreachable. Such thoughts caused my heart to ache like that of a school child with a bad case of puppy love.

❖ ❖ ❖

After completing my normal morning ablutions, I drove to the office, stopping first at McDonald's for a jump start on my daily coffee intake. I arrived at the office at 9:15 a.m., finding Gina and Annie already there. They were seated in the outer office talking about something that seemed to please them both, as they both had a big smile on their faces when I arrived.

"You two seem to be in a good mood this morning," I said. "What are you two talking about?"

Annie didn't say anything. Instead, she pointed to a stack of mail on the corner of her desk that went untouched since it was delivered yesterday. On top of the small pile was an envelope about the size of a greeting card. It was addressed to me, and the return address was from Deana.

"Smell it," Annie instructed as she handed the envelope to me. I complied without giving it a second thought. It was the familiar scent of Deana's perfume. Perhaps I kept it close to my nose too long, or maybe it was the smile that the fragrant scent brought to my face. Whatever the reason, both Annie and Gina started giggling.

"Okay, knock it off you two. We've got a big day ahead of us. Gina, give me a minute to set up in my office, and you can come in and we'll get a head start on the case review."

I opened the door to my office and was impressed by what I saw. An oval conference table borrowed the previous day from an accountant in our building took up a large area of my office.

Four chairs were positioned around the table, and notepads and pens were placed on the table in front of each chair. The large board I've been using to plot the characters was carefully moved onto two metal tripods and positioned at the head of the table before I arrived.

I looked over the set-up and was pleased at the professional appearance and all business atmosphere that was created. I walked around the table and placed my briefcase on my desk, opened it, and removed my gun, placing it in the top right hand drawer of my desk as I've been doing since teaming up with Paul. This time, I placed the gun next to the shoulder holster that I had yet to use.

I sat down and stared at the envelope given to me by Annie. The postmark indicated that it was mailed on Monday. Given the timing of our lunch yesterday and all other things considered, I felt pretty certain it was not a 'Dear John' letter.

I opened the envelope, finding a card with very romantic prose on the front and inside, along with a short note in Deana's handwriting. She ended the note at the bottom of the card with 'To the future.' I carefully placed the card and envelope in my briefcase as if it was a delicate piece of parchment. I allowed my mind to wander into the future with Deana.

❖ ❖ ❖

The knock on my office door jarred me out of my mental journey into a blissful future. "Come in," I yelled. Gina appeared, carrying a carafe of coffee and placed it on the conference table.

"Are you ready, Romeo?" she asked. Ignoring her reference, I indicated that I was and took a seat at the table. Gina joined me, sitting across from me and poured herself a cup of coffee while I finished the cup I brought in.

Gina Russell is the first female investigator Paul ever hired in his 20-plus years of operating a private investigative agency. She was hired 5 years ago when she was just 25 years old.

She earned a degree in criminal justice, after which she joined the police academy. She worked for three years as a police officer for a small department about 30 miles west of Lakewood. She was laid off when the department she worked for was disbanded by the state.

When I first saw her, I thought that she looked a lot like an actress or a model, but she had a very tough, street-wise side to her. As Paul's new partner, I had the opportunity to review her employment file some time ago, which included stellar reviews from the police department as well as from the police academy. She is very proficient with a gun, and is skillful in many other areas involved in police work, including vice. She decided not to seek employment with another police force, wanting instead to hone her investigative skills without having to spend time patrolling the streets.

She became pregnant in her senior year of high school by a young man she hasn't seen since. She has a 13 year-old daughter. The fact that she was a mother played a role in her decision not to continue her police work, as most of the police jobs are in the larger cities with rampant crime and street violence. Aside from moving, she would also be exposing herself to such threats, and did not want to leave her daughter an orphan. She 'recruited herself' into Paul's employment, and the rest, as they say, is history.

I had grown to know and like Gina since I started with Paul, and we worked a number of cases together. I found her to be a great investigator and a wonderful person. Until now, however, Gina had only limited knowledge of the murder case. Her information consisted of what she overheard, saw on my index cards and cork boards, and whatever else I offered during the other investigations we worked together. That was about to change, and I found myself welcoming the opportunity to work with her given her police experience and pleasant nature.

Paul arrived early, and entered my office right away. As soon as he took the seat at the head of the table, I pushed my office door shut and we began. According to the clock in my office, it was 10:05 a.m. Just as intended, we started from the very beginning. We discussed the forensic evidence first, going over all of the official documents we obtained at the start of our involvement in the murder investigation.

First, Paul spread some very graphic pictures taken of the crime scene, along with the three-page coroner's report, across the table. We began with the narrative from the coroner's report. Gina and I focused on the crime scene photographs, leaning into each other from opposite sides of the table to follow along with Paul's narrative. We also managed to obtain about two dozen color copies taken during the autopsy, compliments of a contact we had within the office of the medical examiner:

> The body is that of a well-nourished Caucasian male confirmed to be 52 years old. The body weighs 162 pounds, measuring 72.5 inches from the crown of the head to the sole. The hair on the scalp is dark brown and straight. The irides appear brown with the pupils fixed and dilated. The sclerae and conjunctive are unremarkable, with no evidence of petechial hemorrhages on either. Both upper and lower teeth are natural, and there are no injuries of the gums, cheeks, or lips. There are no deformities, old surgical scars or amputations.
>
> The head is normocephalic, and the eyes, nose and mouth are not remarkable. The neck, front of chest, and abdomen show injuries as described below.
>
> The genitalia are that of a circumcised adult male, and no evidence of injury.
>
> Rigor mortis is fixed. Identification is of the body is by toe tag and the autopsy is not material to identification. The body is not embalmed.

According to the coroner's report, my uncle suffered a total of

38 stab wounds to the chest, abdomen and neck. He also had defensive wounds on both forearms, a deep slash to the fingers and palm of his right hand.

"He grabbed the knife by the blade," Paul said. Of the 38 stab wounds, more than half were determined to be fatal by themselves. He read the description of the neck wound.

"Sharp force injury of neck, left side, transecting the left internal jugular vein. This sharp force injury is complex, and appears to be a combination of a stabbing and cutting wound. It begins on the left side of the neck, at the level of the mid-larynx, over the left sternocleidomastoid muscle; it is gaping, measuring 3 inches in length with smooth edges. Wound dissection determines the path is through the skin, the subcutaneous tissue, and the sternocleidomastoid muscle with hemorrhage along the wound path and transection of the left internal jugular vein. Presented is a gaping stab/incised wound that has clean borders but is not serrated."

He moved to the summary section of the medical examiner's report, excerpting portions.

"A total of 38 stab wounds to the chest, abdomen, including a sharp force wound of neck, right side, with transection of right internal jugular vein. Penetrating stab wounds of chest and abdomen with bilateral hemothorax and hemoperitoneum. Multiple incised wounds of the neck, chest and right hand, which is identified as a defense wound."

"The decedent sustained multiple stab wounds to his upper body concentrated on his chest and abdomen areas. It was determined that of the 38 stab wounds, as many as half were considered fatal, or enough by themselves to cause his death. He had multiple stab wounds to his chest that cut through his ribs and plunged through his aorta and heart."

"The cause of death was listed as exsanguination caused by multiple stab wounds." In other words, my uncle bled to death.

It was at this point that Paul confirmed to Gina what we both already knew. The most important forensic evidence collected at the scene, specifically hair samples, including hair with root attachment, indicated the most likely gender and race of the murderer. Male of African descent, or a Black male perpetrator.

As the application of criminal testing of DNA from evidence collected at crime scenes is still very new, the police are swimming in some murky waters. These findings, however, matched witness statements and other information in our possession, so we considered this suspect depiction seriously.

A review of the police reports in conjunction with the report from the medical examiner indicated that the murder weapon is believed to be a knife with a 6" long blade. It was determined to have a flat edge and a long tapered point. It was never found.

In total, we spent three hours going through all of the initial police and medical reports that a murder generates. Believe me, murder generates a lot of official paperwork.

Just before 1:00 p.m., Annie brought in our lunch, consisting of a large pizza, a salad, and soft drinks from a nearby restaurant. She recoiled at the sight of the 8"x10" color crime scene photographs visible on the table, and nearly dropped the food as she averted her gaze and took an involuntary step backwards.

I gathered the photographs and she placed the food on the table between us, and exited quickly without saying a word. She returned a few seconds later with paper plates and plastic cutlery, but merely handed them through the door without stepping foot back into my office.

Lunch provided us with a natural stopping point to assess all of the evidence and facts known or developed. It gave us a chance to write out the known facts of the murder in a concise, easy to reference fashion. I created a new summary of known facts based on the police reports, the coroner's report, and the general interviews we had conducted since we accepted this assignment late last January. Gina created a written time line that corresponded with my summary of facts. Paul excused himself and returned with a black chalkboard on a tripod that he had stored in his office. He would be creating a 'to do' list.

By 2:00 p.m., we had filled several sheets from our yellow legal pads. As we individually reviewed everything, Paul began a verbal recap of everything we knew about the events of the murder and the deceased, starting with Jerry's activities the day before the murder until his body was found.

"Information from employer. On Tuesday, April 27, 1982, Jerry Stiles arrived at Lakewood Elementary School at 7:45 a.m. to prepare for classes teaching social studies to the seventh and eighth grade students. Fellow teachers noted nothing amiss about his appearance or demeanor. He appeared to be well rested and in a good mood. He spent about ten minutes with two other teachers in the lounge, and then proceeded to his classroom to prepare for the day."

"Now this is interesting," said Paul. "It's something we need to check out further. From the police report, Jerry started his day off early that morning. He had breakfast with a former student of his, a kid named Martin Tingsley. I'm not sure how many teachers keep in close touch with their students like that," Paul added.

"Anyway, according to a combination of accounts from various teachers who had contact with him throughout the day, Jerry completed the day without incident and left the school after finishing his last class at 2:30 p.m." Paul continued.

"Statements from family members. Having recently purchased several pounds of fresh perch, Jerry had invited his brothers and sisters for a family dinner that evening. Invited and in attendance were his brothers Bob and Keith and his wife, and his sisters Bertie and Gwen. Father Stephen, Gwen's son, was also in attendance.

"The dinner party started at 5:00 p.m. and lasted until about 8:00 p.m. Everyone assisted in the clean-up of the kitchen after dinner, leaving the house in immaculate condition. Statements from each of the family members were consistent. Jerry seemed to be in good spirits and nothing appeared to be troubling him. According to the family, Jerry had a habit of going to bed very early and arising early, a fact that was substantiated by the alarm of his clock radio set for 4:30 a.m." Paul flipped back and forth between pages.

"After dinner and everything was clean, the family members left the house, including Bob, who went to Jeanne's house until he had to go to work. He was the last to leave, and the last family member to see Jerry alive. Everybody was gone by 8:30 p.m. At 11:10 p.m., Bob left for his third shift job at General Electric," added Paul.

"According to his time card, he punched in at 11:29 p.m. on Tuesday, April 27 1982 and punched out at 7:32 a.m. on Wednesday the 28th," I interjected.

"Based on statements from his supervisors and the guard at the gate at GE, Bob never left the plant. Consistent with the information from Jerry's employer and peers, Bob's supervisor and fellow third shift employees noted nothing amiss about his appearance or behavior that night. Police detectives also verified the whereabouts of all of the family members through the next morning. None are suspects."

Next, Paul created a narrative based on what we know from combined sources, including the information gleaned from police reports. Here, things began to get very interesting.

"Bob arrived at his residence at about 8:00 a.m. Upon his arrival, he noticed that Jerry's Jeep was parked on the driveway, which was unusual considering that he was always gone by the time Bob returned from work, except on Saturdays. He entered the house through the back door, using his key to unlock the door. When he walked in, he didn't notice anything out of place or unusual in the kitchen.

Before checking on Jerry to see if he decided to take the day off, he fixed himself a drink. A Manhattan, to be exact. He sat at the kitchen table for a few minutes before deciding to check on his brother, after thinking that perhaps Jerry might not have taken the day off, but overslept instead. He left his drink on the table and walked to Jerry's bedroom. The door was shut, so he knocked. When he didn't get an answer, he opened the door. The curtains were drawn shut so he turned on the light. He saw Jerry laying on the bed and the blood soaked bedding. He called Jerry's name, walked to the bed, saw that Jerry was not breathing, ran to the kitchen and called you, Marc, and then called the Lakewood Ambulance Service." Paul paused.

"Apparently Marc, you had a rocket engine strapped to your car because you beat the ambulance and the police by a full 4 minutes, maybe five, it appears." I told Paul that I was dressed and ready for work that morning, so all I had to do was get in my car and go.

"Okay, you all know or have the paperwork from the crime scene investigation, but let's hit a few of the more relevant points, shall we?" Paul asked rhetorically.

"The time of death was affixed at approximately 2:00 a.m. on Wednesday morning, April 28, 1982. The findings from the medical examiner are consistent with the coroner's assessment and the police report. Multiple stab wounds by one assailant, or at least it was only one who committed the murder based on the fingerprints left in blood at the scene. It was classic overkill. It was a frenzied murder. Whoever did this acted in the heat of passion, or anger, or perhaps under the influence of drugs. It was freakin' brutal. Now we can learn a few things that might help us piece together the events of that night. And this is where it starts to get a bit dicey," Paul said, before continuing.

"Continuing on with the crime scene, Jerry was found naked in his bed. His clothes were folded neatly in a pile by the bed. Based on everything we know, the assailant was either someone he invited in, possibly to stay over for the night, or someone he let inside, as there were no signs of forced entry. Believe, me, the police looked carefully at this. Also, the perpetrator likely knew that Bob was the only other resident of the house, and most likely knew that he would not be home until about eight o'clock that morning. That explains the fact that the killer felt comfortable taking a shower before he left the scene. For all anyone knows, the killer could have made himself breakfast and cleaned up after. At any rate, he was very sure of himself."

"And now we have the bizarre. There was evidence that sexual activity took place in the bedroom before, during or perhaps even after the attack. Semen was found on the bed sheet, on the floor, and on a washcloth mixed with blood. We have no idea who it belongs to."

Paul paused for a minute, allowing for the full effect of what he just said to sink in. Although I had known about this, Gina didn't. In the stillness of the room, I was replaying the final scenes of the 1970's movie *Looking For Mr. Goodbar* in my mind, changing Diane Keaton into my uncle, and her New York City apartment into my old bedroom. The song *Don't Leave Me This Way*, from the movie's soundtrack began playing in my head. It's funny how one's mind works sometimes.

Breaking the uncomfortable silence, Paul continued. "There is something that was noted at the scene but not expanded upon in the police notes.," he said.

"Transfer blood stains were found inside the top drawer of Jerry's dresser, and others inside the top two drawers of his nightstand. It appears that after Jerry was murdered, the killer opened the drawers and was looking for something. Maybe money, maybe a change of clothes, or maybe something else. If it was money, whoever rummaged through the drawers missed a pretty obvious bank envelope with fifty bucks inside. Also, Jerry's closet was ransacked, but nothing appeared to have been taken. A large glass container of quarters about the size of a mayonnaise jar, clearly visible, was left untouched by the killer."

Paul continued his dissertation. "Even more significantly, Jerry always wore a white gold ring on the ring finger of his left hand. The ring has one large diamond and two smaller diamonds on either side. It was appraised at $5,025 just a month before his murder. Two of the two smaller diamonds belonged to Jerry's grandmother, Marc's great-grandmother on his father's side. Anyway, the killer left it on his finger. Although it was covered in blood, there is no evidence that the killer tried to remove it after death. So, a 'normal' type of robbery could be ruled out.

Now, it's also interesting that the killer left the room, walked to Bob's bedroom, removed the bedspread from his bed and placed it over Jerry. For whatever reason, the killer stabbed Jerry at least three more times through this bedspread. These were identified as post-mortem wounds."

Paul looked up at Gina and over to me. "Any thoughts?" he asked.

"Frenzied overkill for sure," Gina said.

"Ditto," I added.

"Judging by the wounds and the ME's report, it's apparent that Jerry saw what was coming. He was awake, or awakened, as the attack began. This is shown by the defensive wounds and the really bad wound on his right hand, where he grabbed the blade of the knife either as the attack was beginning or at some point before he sustained the fatal wound. That's about as much of a struggle that he was able to put up against his attacker.

The trajectory of the knife, Jerry's stab wounds indicate that he was stabbed while he, the attacker, or both were in various positions. The post-mortem wounds were probably done when the murderer was most likely standing next to the bed. By the way, Jerry's BAC, or blood alcohol level was .28. He had a lot to drink before he was killed. He would have been, or should have been, quite drunk."

Gina interjected with a question. "Did the family say that he was he drinking heavily at the dinner, or after dinner?'

"According to the family, Jerry was starting to drink much more than ever before. He went from buying gin by the fifth to the gallon. His drink of choice was gin and tonic. According to the family, Jerry was feeling pretty good by the time everyone left, but was not falling down drunk. As the family assumed that he was going to go to bed after they left, no one worried about him."

Although I had poured over the case file and none of this information was news to me, it was good to hear someone else provide the narrative. I knew there was much more to come.

"According to information obtained from interviews conducted by police in 1982 and by Marc more recently of the neighbors, some other odd things were noted. Based on the collective information provided by the neighbors, at least two neighbors saw Jerry come home from work at his usual time. They also witnessed the arrival of the dinner guests and the multiple cars present at the residence through about 8:00 or so that night. By 8:30 p.m. or so, everybody was gone, which is consistent with the information provided by the family. Then it starts to get a bit weird."

At this point, I pulled the typed interview of the next door neighbor from the case folder, anticipating what Paul was about to say.

"According to Mrs. Victoria Slythe, the neighbor who lives in the house directly west of Jerry's house, she saw three odd things that night. Two of the three things were corroborated by Mr. Elgin, another neighbor. We'll address these events in chronological order," Paul said.

"First, sometime *during* the dinner party, two young boys, both white and both appearing to be in their early teens, were seen standing, and then sitting in the back yard of the residence. They were only there for a few minutes, according to both neighbors, and then disappeared though the brush behind the residence, as if they were walking away from the house and off the property. None of the family members reportedly saw these two young men."

"The next unusual thing noticed by the two neighbors was the arrival of a red vintage corvette parked at Jerry's house, at approximately 9:00 p.m. Although neither neighbor got the plate number, both believed that it was an out of state plate.

Neither saw the driver or Jerry, just the car. According to Mrs. Slythe, the car was gone at 9:30 p.m., but back again at about 11:00

p.m., or when her television show was over and she was about to watch the local news.

From her chair in her living room, she had a good view of the driveway and Jerry's house. Oh, one more thing we learned from the neighbors, Jerry did leave in his own vehicle at least once after dinner, possibly sometime between 9:30 and 10:30 that night."

"Sounds like Grand-freakin' Central Station," Gina blurted.

"Thank goodness for nosy neighbors who get the times correct by their favorite television shows," I said.

"Well, as you know, Marc, this is where things begin to take another dark turn. Real dark, as a matter of fact, and questions into these events have not been received too well by the police. They've kept a lot of things secret from your family as you now know all too well. The question is why, because it certainly was not to protect your uncle's image, or protect your family. There's something else going on, and you know it. That's the reason that from now on, you damn well better be using the shoulder holster I gave you, and start carrying your gun. There's something wrong."

Subconsciously putting my hand where my holstered gun should have been, I blurted "Yeah, I know Paul."

"Gina, from now on you don't go anywhere without your piece either, am I clear on that?" Paul said in a stern, almost father-like fashion.

"Yes boss!" Gina snapped.

"Thanks to a lot of arm twisting, Detective McCarty finally gave up a lot of his investigative notes to us. Well, he didn't give them up as much as we sort of 'borrowed' copies of them from the station, courtesy of Pete, my contact there. Anyway, because of this bit of playing spy, we know where he went the night before he was murdered, and we have a good handle on many of his activities that night and even in the weeks and months before the murder.

"But before we talk about that, I want to set the scene of Jerry's other life, or what we know about it, first."

By this time, I had almost finished a pack of cigarettes and drank two carafes of coffee. Gina did the same. It was now 2:45 p.m., and Paul suggested we take a break until 3:00, which would give us time for a much needed bathroom break and to handle anything of consequence that had arisen during the meeting.

❖ ❖ ❖

After returning from the men's room where I splashed a copious amount of cold water on my face, I returned to my office feeling a bit more refreshed. Paul and Gina retreated to their respective offices. In their absence, I removed the romantic card from my briefcase and read the prose and note from Deana. I wondered how there could be so much ugliness in the world when there is so much beauty.

I decided to call Deana at her office, hoping before I picked up the receiver that she would have a few minutes free to talk. After two rings, she answered. It was so good to hear her voice. For the next three minutes, we talked about our last lunch and I told her that I was just given the card that she sent me in the mail. I thanked her for thinking of me, and for making my day.

"How's the meeting going?" she asked.

"You really don't want to know. Pretty crappy stuff. Sad, actually. But you and your beauty are carrying me through."

"That's sweet. Maybe we can sneak away for lunch again soon?" she asked.

"How about tomorrow. It's Friday. Maybe we can also meet up for happy hour?"

"Hey, don't push it," she said, snickering.

"May I pick you up tomorrow at 11:30?" I asked.

"That would be great."

"Great, until tomorrow" I said, just above a whisper.

"Until tomorrow." The line went dead, and I replaced the handset back on the cradle.

❖ ❖ ❖

Paul and Gina returned to my office, and we sat back at the conference table. This time, Gina sat next to me for easier access to the investigative folder. Paul moved from his former position at the head of the oval table to a spot directly across from us. I didn't see him sneak in a new 4' x 6' cork board, which surprised me as it is rather difficult to miss given its size. He had placed it against the wall behind him. It had a small red bow on the corner. Paul pointed to the board and smiled as he said that he bought me a present.

"Marc, you're gonna need it. Based on our findings, as you have determined from the investigation you conducted since we accepted this assignment, we're actually conducting two parallel investigations. The common factor of both is *murder*." He placed particular emphasis on the word "murder."

For the next forty-five minutes, we began a review of our initial incursion into the dark underbelly of the homosexual community. Paul set the stage by providing a verbal recap of the public life of my uncle, or the man known to me and my family.

"Jerry was a well-educated and highly respected man in the community. He worked with children and young teens. He was a former principle, but decided to return to teaching. He was active in the Catholic church.

"Socially, he outwardly appeared to be a 'man's man.' There was nothing the least bit effeminate about him. He often dated women, but claimed that he never found the 'right' woman. He was very close to an elderly woman named Millie, who Jerry considered to be his step-mother. Millie was very protective of Jerry, and they spent a lot of time together around the holidays. Yet Millie was somewhat of an outsider as she never became involved in any of the normal family functions.

"Then there was a man by the name of Walter Houghton. Walter Houghton was close in age to Jerry and teaches at a junior high school in the Miami-Dade County School District. Young teens. Walter and Jerry had been friends since their army days, and their relationship remained strong despite the 1200 or so miles that existed between Lakewood and Miami, Florida. Walter and Jerry would visit and stay with each other during school breaks and in the summer.

"In 1977, Walter Houghton purchased an estate in Miami and moved in. It was well known within the family that Jerry was paying a portion of the mortgage to Walter every month, which was about $200 each month, as Jerry planned on moving to Miami after taking an early retirement he had planned when he reached 55. That would have been just a few years after he was murdered. Despite all of the obvious signs and indications, Jerry's family did not know, or choose to believe that Jerry was a homosexual." Paul paused while he continued to review his notes.

"They did not look upon his relationship with Walter as a homosexual relationship, for there was never any outward displays of affection between the two men," he added.

"According to police reports and information provided to us by the family, the only family member who knew with certainty that Jerry was living a double life was Father Stephen, a Catholic priest. He is Jerry's nephew and Marc's cousin. He knew that Jerry was leading a double life, one of a man who outwardly appeared to be a successful professional held in high regard in the community, an unencumbered and carefree bachelor.

His other life was that of a closet homosexual, a man who was in a long-term committed relationship with Walter Houghton, a man considered to be his equal.

"About 12-18 months before he was murdered, however, Jerry's brothers and sisters began to see a change in his behavior. Although the signs were subtle at first, Jerry began drinking heavily. He began to take unnecessary chances, and wrecked at least one car when he hit a tree while driving drunk.

"There were other signs as well, that in retrospect, should have caused warning bells to sound. Noticing this change in behavior, his sisters asked Father Stephen to talk to him, to find out what was wrong. Jerry apparently spoke freely to Father Stephen about his lifestyle, not because of his family connection, but because Father Stephen was bound to silence by the seal of the Catholic church. In some ways, it seemed that Jerry enjoyed being able to spill his guts out to Father Stephen knowing that there was not a damn thing he could say to the family. It was as if Jerry had a special power over Father Stephen, a power that was sanctioned by the Vatican. Marc, you know all about that as you attended the seminary."

At this point I spoke up. "Yeah Paul, but I apparently missed that class. But as you know, I was not that close to my uncle. I would see him at family functions and when I stopped to see my dad on those rare occasions, especially when I was married and right after the birth of my son. I remember bringing my wife, well, we weren't married yet, to a family get-together in the summer of 1979. Uncle Jerry was hammered, as were others there to a lesser degree, including my own father. Jerry was relentlessly talking about my intended, telling her to take off her shirt and dance on the top of the picnic table.

"She is pretty big in the chest department if you know what I mean, a fact that was not lost on Uncle Jerry. His behavior and comments then were quite obnoxious and out of character.

"Looking back, it is obvious that he was over compensating, putting on a manly front, perhaps for my benefit. I blew it off back then, but I can see now that it was all an act."

Just then, Gina chimed in with a question that sounded more like an accusation. "Are you telling me that he had his whole family fooled? No one aside from the priest knew he was a homosexual? Nobody, not even the slightest suspicion?"

"Well, Gina, that's how my family handled such matters. I think you'll find that my family was not alone in turning a blind eye to the unpleasant or the unthinkable. Just think about Rock Hudson," I said.

I also relayed a story I heard just after the murder. "Gina, I told Paul about this, but we should all have this on record now, together. Shortly after the murder, my father told me about an incident that took place in the late summer or fall before Jerry was murdered. It was in late 1981. Walter came to Lakewood from Miami to surprise Jerry. Instead, it was Walter who was surprised. Apparently, he walked in on Jerry with a young man. A very young man, a teenager, in his bed.

"Although Walter was upset, it was Jerry who became obnoxious and uncontrollable. Jerry bragged that he had a 'stable of fresh meat' for his sexual appetite. He claimed that he could get as many young men as he wanted. My dad was unaware of this until right after the funeral when Walter Houghton pulled him aside and told him. My father refused to believe Walter, and this put a strain on Walter's relationship with the family. After all, decent people don't talk about these types of things."

Paul interjected, "Speaking of things decent people don't talk about, Marc, there is the matter of U.S. Army papers and newspaper clippings that your dad found packed away in Jerry's possessions in the attic."

"What clippings, what papers?" asked Gina. "This is the first I've heard about those."

"These." Paul produced and opened a manila envelope with old papers in various sizes, many turned brown from age. These were found in Jerry's packed belongings.

"Jerry was in the military and served in Korea. He was part of some secret military or intelligence project that involved psychological conditioning. What's left of his writings gives a glimpse into his life in the military, and includes torture, murder, and sexual sadism, all courtesy of our own government and the North Koreans."

"What in the world are you talking about?" Gina asked. "What does this have to do with his murder? Been watching too many science fiction movies, Paul?"

"I wish. Marc and I spent a lot of time researching what we could about Jerry's military history, and the mind experiments conducted by the military during the 1950's and beyond. We've done our best to figure out what Jerry was involved in, but we've hit stone walls everywhere we've turned. What we discovered is that many of the same people involved in some of the same projects are located in and around Lakewood. And many have powerful positions. We got some names from Jerry's writings, but not much survived over the last 30 years."

"You're going to have to do better than that, Paul," Gina said. "I'm still lost."

"We have reason to believe that Jerry was a participant in programs that involved psychological conditioning, or mind control when he was in the army during Korea. It was a clandestine project that began with World War II that few knew existed. From Jerry's notes he took when in the military, there are indications that he was abused, and that includes sexual abuse.

"Whether or not his sexual proclivities were the result of such abuse, or whether his sexual preference made him a candidate for the programs that ultimately involved the abuse is unknown. No one is talking. Whatever happened back then, may, in fact, have played a part, or maybe led up to the behavior that got him killed."

"Or it might not have anything whatsoever to do with the murder," Gina replied.

"Right, but just keep all of this in the back of your mind," urged Paul, who continued. "Now fast forward from there to five years ago. More and more, Jerry seemed to be leading a double life. His 'normal' personal and professional life on one hand, and on the other, some type of alternate personality. One of darkness, of perversion, of evil. He was unraveling and seemingly losing control.

"It was as if he was involved in a fight between dueling personalities. He was walking a 'yellow brick road' of darkness."

"You're getting pretty far out there, don't you think, Paul? asked

Gina.

"I hope so, but that remains to be seen."

The silence that lingered in the room momentarily was broken when Gina spoke up. "For now, why don't we just stick to the basic facts as we know them. Let's forget the psycho-babble stuff for now. A brutal murder was committed five years ago. There was ample forensic evidence collected at the scene to identify the perpetrator. All that is needed to match a person with the evidence. At the outset, the police, and especially Detective McCarty stated that they were confident in solving the case in a day or two. So now, over five years later, no arrests have been made. It's really just that simple."

"It *might well* be that simple, Gina, and I hope it is," Paul said. "I had a couple of meetings with my contact at the district attorney's office." Paul continued.

"Marc already knows about this, but I'll tell you now. They are not at all happy about our involvement. Not in the least. They don't want us poking our noses into anything. And it's not just because Marc once dated the district attorney's wife in another life." Paul made it a point to emphasize my involvement with the D.A.'s wife.

Hearing that Paul knew about my previous exploits, and now Gina knows, I slowly slumped down in my chair. It was true that I had dated Sarah in the 70's, now the present wife of the current D.A. It was during my wild time, and I was less than nice in my unceremonious dismissal of her. There was always a heaviness in my heart, a feeling of regret, because of the way I treated her. There was a much more palpable heaviness whenever I had the occasion to deal with the district attorney, for it is certain he knew this history. Oh what a small world and even smaller community, I thought to myself. Skeletons in closets don't like to be confined. They're always rattling to get out. Perhaps the resident skeletons of Lakewood closets might be beating on their respective doors, just waiting for us to release them.

Paul continued his animated narration. "Anyway, forget about Marc's mischief. It's well beyond that. The district attorney's office has essentially taken over the Lakewood PD investigation of Jerry's homicide. And somewhere in all of this the feds have their noses in this as well. The D.A.'s office, though, is calling the shots now. My sources from the police and the D.A.'s office have both said this is rather unusual. There's something we're not supposed to see, or find."

"Does that mean that someone does not want Jerry's murderer to be identified? Do you think that someone high up is throttling the investigation?" asked Gina.

"Maybe, but I don't think it's quite that simple. There's something else going on. Much bigger. Much more nefarious. Whether or not it involves Jerry's murder in any direct fashion remains to be seen. Regardless, my buddy at the D.A.'s office told me that people in high places in the police department and even at his office are real nervous right now. So are some other high profile people in our neck of the woods. My best source at Lakewood PD told me that our involvement could shorten our life spans considerably, should we continue to probe deeper," Paul said.

"Marvelous," I said. "So if we continue our current investigation, it's gonna get ugly. Sorry, but I'm not going to be intimidated by anybody. I say we double down. Let's put everything we got into this. No guts, no glory."

"I'm all in," said Gina.

"So, it's unanimous," said Paul.

"Okay, I guess I'll ask the obvious, which I assume would have been addressed long before this if we had a particular suspect in mind. Were there any black men in Jerry's life, I mean, close friends?" Gina asked.

"None that we know of, at least not known friends or associates," Paul said.

As we continued our meeting, Gina still had questions. Specifically, she wanted to know where Jerry went hours before he was murdered.

Paul spoke up, saying "I was wondering when you'd ask that. Jerry was seen at Bucking Bronco's Books, the adult book store located at the county line. I've got a copy of a report written by McCarty who interviewed the owner and who was on duty that night. Bill 'Bucky' Phillips. He admitted that Jerry was a regular customer. Under duress, or so it reads between the lines, Phillips admitted to McCarty that his shop occasionally served as a meeting place for homosexuals to find 'dates.' On the night of his murder, Jerry met a man there who drove a red 1966 vintage corvette. They left the place at the same time."

"Do they know who that man is?" asked Gina.

"Yeah, a native of Lakewood. Benjamin Cooper. Name ring any bells?" asked Paul.

"No, not offhand," replied Gina.

"He was a bigwig in the steel industry, until that industry started to die off. He sold his company to a Chinese firm and mysteriously, he supposedly made a fortune. He owns a jewelry store now. It could be a front business, but a front for what I don't know. The police deny that he's a suspect in the murder, though. According to McCarty's report, Cooper met Jerry in a particular section of bookstore that also doubles as pick-up spot for those 'in the know.' Based on the police report, it did not seem like a 'chance' encounter, though. It seemed that the meet-up was planned."

"According to Phillips, he overheard Jerry talking about some 'homemade' photographs he had at his house. Just then, a black man walked into the bookstore and walked back toward Jerry and Cooper. The black man and Cooper seemed to know each other, or at least that's the way it seemed based on the account from Phillips, who denies ever seeing him before."

"Now that's interesting on a number of levels," said Gina.

"As a matter of fact, Cooper denies knowing or even seeing the black man there. McCarty interviewed him a few times, and each time his story is the same. He never saw the other guy."

"Does McCarty believe him?" Gina asked.

"Hard to tell, but my gut says no."

"So Jerry left with Cooper, or at they left at the same time. Cooper admits visiting Jerry at his house, supposedly because of his curiosity about the homemade pictures," recounted Gina.

"Right. According to Cooper, Jerry wanted sex from Cooper before he would show him the pictures, but he was not interested. Apparently, Jerry was not Cooper's cup of tea, or maybe it was all about the pictures and nothing else. In any case, Jerry returned to the bookstore alone about an hour later, which matches the neighbors' accounts and Cooper's story. Well, it almost matches Cooper's account."

"Cooper did not tell the whole truth to the police. While they discounted him as the killer, he's lying about some of the facts of that night. He gave a statement that he merely followed Jerry home once, then left shortly after Jerry made his advances. In his first interview with McCarty, Cooper denied seeing any photographs and left because of Jerry's advances."

"In subsequent interviews, Cooper ultimately admitted that he did see a large collection of photographs. He told the police that Jerry had quite a collection of pictures of young men in various compromising positions. Most were of photographs that Jerry had supposedly taken. Cooper then told the police that he was not interested in what Jerry had to offer, and left. According to Cooper, that night was the first time he met Jerry, and the last time he ever saw him."

"But what about the neighbor saying that she saw Cooper's car back at Jerry's house at 11:00 p.m., after her television program was over?" Gina asked.

"Exactly," Paul said. "His car was reportedly seen back at Jerry's at that time, which indicates a second visit, considering the improbability of there being two different guys driving a red corvette visiting the house where a murder was committed."

"And Cooper still denies this second visit?"

"He sure does. And McCarty talked to Cooper's wife about his activities that night. Her name is Sadie Cooper, a real 'uppity' upper class kind of woman, according to Mack. Her statement is consistent with her husband's account, at least with respect to the time. She is adamant, though, that her husband was tricked by Jerry, that he thought he was going to look at Jerry's collection of cars, or photographs of them, that are being stored in Florida. She claims that Jerry is a car buff, which is obvious, and that Jerry was interested in buying a vintage muscle car from the south. One that had never been driven in snow."

"Does Mack think she actually believes that, or is she covering for her husband?"

"McCarty said that she seems dumber than a box of rocks, in his words, but how much does it really matter? He's been eliminated as the murderer by forensics and has an alibi for the time of the murder. The book hasn't been closed on him, though, but Mack just doesn't see much of any other connection."

"What about the other man, the black man that Cooper seemed to know?" Gina asked.

"This is where it even gets stranger. Even Mack can't account for this part of the night. Phillips insisted that Cooper and the unidentified black man appeared to know each other, but ultimately admitted that was his perception. He's got no proof or anything else to back up his assessment. Phillips is not the best witness, according to McCarty.

"However, that does not change the fact that this guy was in the store. Also, it's more than coincidence that the forensics indicate that hair found at the murder scene, including and especially in the shower and shower drain are from a black man."

"So at this point we're certain, or at least reasonably certain that it was the black man, or a black man, who committed the murder," Gina said.

"Yes."

"What happened to him after Jerry and Cooper left the bookstore?"

"Phillips said that he left, almost right behind them. Never saw him again."

"Could he describe him?"

"We have a general description, but nothing of any significance. Mid-to-late 30's, about 6' tall, thin build, closely cropped black hair. Dressed in jeans and a dark colored hoodie type sweatshirt. Again, nothing real usable," I said.

"Remember, other unmatched prints were found at the scene. We can be relatively sure that we're looking for a black male suspect, but is he the *only* suspect? Did he act alone? Jerry had no history of having any other 'partners' outside of his own race. So it would certainly be out of character, but not impossible," added Paul.

"This whole thing with Cooper really bothers me. Too close to the murderer, or so it seems, and to the victim. He's guilty of *something*, at least that's what I suspect. I'm not sure of what yet, but I can feel it. I don't trust him, or his connections or influence in this town," I said.

"And get this, there's yet another twist to this case that is a real mind bender. There was a murder of a man who worked as a furniture salesman for a high-end store in Lakewood.

"His name was Graham Martz, age 49. He was killed on Saturday, June 26, 1982, just two months after my uncle was murdered. His body was found on an incline leading to the lake. He had been stabbed over 20 times with a similar sized knife. Although the media didn't report what I'm about to tell you, I learned about this from my former partner when I worked rescue. In fact, I almost caught the call myself, but I was running back-up as I was leaving the squad anyway. My partner comes back from the call and tells me the guy was 'Code 11,' meaning he had assumed room temperature.

"Anyway, this Graham Martz was found lying face up with his pants around his ankles. There were similar stab wounds on his upper body, including defensive wounds. There was also evidence that he was having sex with someone, presumably, where he was found."

Gina interjected, "I remember that case. I thought they caught the guy who did it."

"They did. They arrested and later convicted a guy by the name of Barry Newman, a 31-year-old white male who worked briefly with Martz. But here's an interesting fact that was never reported anywhere. I found this out from Jenkins during one of our nights out at Rossi's. You know they found various prints inside Jerry's bedroom that did not appear to be connected to the murder. Well, a match tuned up when they ran Newman's prints against those found in Jerry's bedroom. So, Newman, the white guy who killed Martz, was inside of Jerry's bedroom at some point before the murder. It could have been days, weeks, who knows. But his prints were there. The cops interrogated Newman pretty extensively. Here's another twist. Newman, it was learned, was dating my cousin around the same time of my uncle's murder."

"Come again?" Gina blurted. "This is getting pretty difficult to follow."

"Tell me about it," I said. "Before you ask, Newman was sentenced to life in prison. McCarty wanted the D.A. to give him something to bargain with and interrogate Newman about Jerry's murder. The D.A. refused. McCarty went anyway, but with nothing to bargain with, Newman had no motivation to talk."

"My head's going to explode guys," Gina said, appearing exasperated. "Is there anything else you're going to spring on me? I can see why you need another board. So with all of this happening here locally, why would you think Walter Houghton has anything at all to do with Jerry's murder?"

Paul chimed in. "It's unlikely that there's any direct connection, but Walter certainly knows a lot more than he's telling. He knows what was going on in Jerry's life at the time of the murder. He's got names, I'm sure. He knows who's who here in Lakewood."

"The Martz murder really bothers me," I said. "It sure seems like there's some kind of network here, and my gut is telling me that Houghton might well be part of it."

"That's the reason I told Mary Clayburn that we'd be talking to a 'person of interest' in Florida," Paul added. Maybe the word would get to Houghton, and he would start to talk to others up here who were connected to Jerry. Then we'll see who might be getting nervous."

"What about the more sensible route, talking to Father Stephen?" asked Gina.

"Marc already tried to talk with Father Stephen, and so did I. We got nowhere. He's playing the role of a deaf mute."

"Doesn't Jerry's death release him from the vow of silence, Marc?" asked Gina.

"Apparently not in this case," I replied. "I think there's so much more under the surface."

Myself, Paul and Gina spent the next hour going through the remaining pieces of evidence that seemed to be of lesser value to the case. There wasn't anything we did not address or any aspect of the case we left untouched. In addition to the twists and turns of events, we were in awe at the lack of active investigation being conducted by the Lakewood Police Department and the district attorney's office. Everything seemed to get shut down a within a few months after their initial investigation. They weren't even going through the motions anymore. And that, we all agreed, was troublesome.

It was just after 5:00 p.m. when we concluded our meeting. Paul left the office to have dinner with his wife. I told him I'd be in tomorrow morning to go over the big theft case for Aetna, and asked Gina if she would give me a hand. She agreed.

"C'mon Gina, I'll buy you a cold one," I said to her as she was gathering her notes.

"I've got to take a rain check. I need to get back to look after my daughter tonight, otherwise I would. I'll see you in the morning. I'll be in about eight."

After wishing her good night, I sat down at my desk, my mind was spinning at the events of the day.

Annie had left the office right at 5:00 p.m., and turned the phones over to the answering service. I sat at my desk, pulled the card from my briefcase and reread it again.

After several minutes of reflection and anticipating my lunch tomorrow, I decided to call it a night. I stopped at the Towne Bar on my way back to my apartment. Brenda saw me come in and had my usual waiting for me on the bar before I sat down.

For happy hour, the bar was virtually empty, except for the restaurant side. There, waitresses were busily serving food to couples and families. Seeing smiles on their faces, couples holding hands over candlelight, I began to long for such companionship and a happy future. Yet, it seemed unreachable.

I downed my first two drinks in silence, making a mental recap of the facts we had discussed in our meeting today. After waiting on a small party of well-dressed businessmen at the other end of the bar, Brenda walked over to me and brought me another drink.

"This one's on me," she said. "You look like you're a thousand miles away. Are you alright? How's the murder case going?" I told Brenda only the most basic of details, and occasionally use her as a sounding board for my personal problems.

"Trust me kiddo, you don't want to know." She smiled and agreed, adding that murder makes her uncomfortable.

"Yeah, me too," I said.

I left the Towne Bar and was back at my apartment by 8:30 p.m. I grabbed a beer from the refrigerator and sat on the couch, planning to catch some television before going to sleep. Before I could change clothes, sleep overcame me.

CHAPTER 4

Friday, May 1, 1987

I was the first to arrive at the office at 7:05 a.m. with a newly found feeling of invigoration and determination along with a full, extra-large cup of coffee to jump start my day. I was facing a full case load of insurance related fraud cases, not the least of which was the federal judge claiming an incredible loss. The burden of these cases allowed me a short mental break from my obsession with my uncle's murder. I figured that this was the calm before the storm, and soon, I would know that I figured correctly.

There was an unreleased news story sitting on some editor's desk at the Lakewood Press that I was sure would ruffle the feathers of some local residents. Paul had assumed a consulting role in the murder case, for which I was grateful. Yet, I couldn't help but wonder if Paul was as dedicated as I was to finding the killer. After all, I had done nearly all of the field investigation to date, including all of the interviews with the local people in Lakewood. Thankfully, Gina was now committed to the case, giving me another set of eyeballs and some solid investigative support.

Regardless of the gloom surrounding the current cases and our premier murder case, I found solace in my upcoming lunch with the woman of my dreams.

In preparation for my lunch, I was wearing my favorite bright pink and red striped tie that reminds me of a candy cane. I turned on the table top radio I kept in my office. Instead of the quiet, classical music I often kept on quietly in the background, the speakers turned out the current hit *Livin' on a Prayer* by Bon Jovi a bit louder than I liked. Apparently, the cleaning staff had changed the station while moving the conference table back to its home inside the accountant's office and while they cleaned our offices. I sat down anyway, as I found some of the lyrics to mimic the way I was feeling. "You live for the fight when it's all that you got... For love, we'll give it a shot..."

As I soaked in the song, I proceeded with my morning ritual of placing my briefcase on my desk and moving my .38 into the top right-hand drawer of my desk. I then removed the card from Deana and re-read the words and her note, just to make sure nothing had changed. I stared at the card for two, perhaps three more songs before I returned it to its proper spot in my briefcase and changed the station on the radio.

Looking down, I noticed that I didn't close the drawer after placing my gun inside. I stared at the gun, along with the shoulder holster that Paul had given me. I contemplated whether I should put it on under my coat today. Deep down inside, I felt as if I was "livin' on a prayer." There was something bothering me, I just could not put my finger on it.

❖ ❖ ❖

I heard the office door open just before 8:00 a.m. Annie entered first, followed by Gina. Annie turned on the lights in the reception area and called our answering service, taking the phones back from the service and retrieving any messages. Annie seemed to be taking a long time with the service, which is rarely a good sign. Right after hanging up the phone, Annie walked in to my office and stood silently in front of my desk.

"I've got a few messages for you, Marc, that came in after hours yesterday." Eying the desk drawer that was still open and the gun inside, she said "I'll give you the messages as long as you remember I'm just the messenger, and you shouldn't shoot the messenger, okay?"

She placed four white pieces of paper torn from our office message pad on my desk, and put a recently opened roll of Rolaids on top of the papers. For whatever reason, I thought about our system of record keeping for a second, wondering if it was a good idea of keeping a copy of all incoming messages. The white copy goes to the recipient while the yellow copy stays in the book to create a permanent record. Obviously, the careful and thoughtful placement of the Rolaids was self-explanatory. I paused before I picked up the slips of paper, giving Annie enough time to exit my office, shutting my door behind her.

The first message was from Paige Vetter, the Aetna claims adjuster handling the federal judge's case. She wanted an immediate update as the judge was insisting that the company reimburse him for his loss before the end of business today.

The second message was from the judge himself who obviously kept my business card and called yesterday to demand that I furnish him with my investigative report concerning his claim. Yes, demand.

The third message was from Mary Clayburn, who said that an extensive article was on schedule to appear in tomorrow's edition of *The Lakewood Daily News* and it would be, in her words, 'quite a zinger.' Whatever that meant.

The message on the bottom of the pile was from Deana, who apologized that she would not be able to make our lunch date today as her son came down with the flu and she would not be at work. For a moment, I wondered if that was true or whether she was having second thoughts about me and us. Perhaps I was moving too fast, pushing too hard.

I sat in silence for the next several minutes, wondering if she was keeping true to her stated desire of not wanting to enter into any new relationship so soon after her last one ended. I popped two Rolaids into my mouth and considered the new opening in my schedule for today. I was depressed. No, I was crushed. I decided that I would wait until later in the day to call Deana at home to check on her son and get a feel for things. Meanwhile, I had work to do.

At 8:30, I asked Gina to come into my office so we could review the case of the federal judge and his missing trinkets and boat of a car. As she walked in to my office, she quietly whispered "I'm sorry about your plans today, Marc." I pretended I did not hear her and tossed the claim file on my desk, and asked her to sit down and review the inroads I made so far.

The review took about forty-five minutes. Her conclusion was simple, "It stinks." We both agreed that something was not right with the claim, and everything about it was too tidy. Like me, Gina is not a fan of 'tidy.'

I told Gina that we were running out of time as the insurance company had a specific window to either deny or pay the claim. I was already getting heat from the claims adjuster from Aetna as well as the judge, and we had no reason to recommend denying the claim except for our gut instincts. The car and the jewelry that was inside is still missing. Unless or until we had something tangible to present to Aetna, I was going to have to close our file out and let them decide what to do, based on the evidence.

"What, you suddenly lost all of your spunk, Marc?" Gina chided me. "Let's go out and shake some trees to see what falls out. Let's go do something, anything, to see who we can shake up. We can re-interview some of the neighbors, maybe they might crack under my crafty interviewing skills. Come on, let's go!" I reluctantly agreed to give the investigation another shot based on Gina's enthusiasm, which was beginning to become contagious.

As we were preparing to leave, I opened my desk drawer and put on my shoulder holster, tucking my .38 snugly inside. "Now you look like Dan Tanna," Gina said, referring to the fictional television character of the hit television series *Vega$*. "And I suppose you're Phyllis, his lovely assistant. Well, my .38 is not quite his .357 magnum, and my 1981 Chrysler LeBaron is no match against his 57 T-Bird."

As we were about to leave, Paul walked into the outer office carrying a small cardboard box. He then walked into my office and handed both Gina and I a 'pager,' a device about the size of a pack of cigarettes that was assigned a specific number that when called, would emit a series of 'beeps.' Each pager has its number on a sticker on the side of the unit, and a clip where it could be attached to one's belt. "Here, if I need you, I'll call your pager number and you can call the office," Paul said. "Thanks, Paul, great idea," I replied, as he walked out of the office. I looked at the device and tossed it in my drawer where my gun used to be. Closing the drawer, I looked up at Gina and said "Let's go."

It took Gina only about 5 hours of working in the field to 'break' the case of the federal judge. As it turned out, he's not as smart as he thinks he is. Approaching the claim from a different perspective, Gina suggested that we conduct some surveillance of the judge. We knew his schedule from my previous interviews, and obtained his honor's court schedule from the roster posted at the federal court house.

Normally, surveillance is a long, tedious and frankly, quite boring activity. It generally involves hours and even days of waiting and watching, trying to be inconspicuous, while trying to keep one's liquid intake to a minimum to avoid the unpleasant task of peeing into a jar while seated inside a car or a van. It usually consists of long periods of inactivity followed by a period of sheer frenzy when something does happen.

Today would prove to be one of those rare exceptions where things happened 'just right.'

After identifying the judge's vehicle parked in the space reserved for him, we set up surveillance from a nearby location. We spotted the judge leaving for lunch at 11:20 a.m., which was consistent with the posted court docket. I maneuvered my non-descript gray LeBaron behind him in traffic, thinking that perhaps he was headed to home for lunch with his wife. Instead, he turned in the opposite direction of his house.

We followed the judge to a florist, where Gina took several pictures of him exiting the store carrying a large bouquet of flowers. From there, we followed him to a private residence located in an upscale neighborhood of Lakewood, although not as classy or upscale as where he resides with his wife and children. Gina continued taking pictures, using our 35 mm camera with a zoom lens.

We watched the judge exit his car and carry the flowers to the front door of the house with the nicely manicured lawn. We could see a young lady answer the door. Upon seeing the judge, she stuck her head outside and looked up and down the street, as if she was checking to see if he was followed. Certain that he wasn't she threw her arms around him and planted a great big kiss on his lips, all caught on film by Gina.

"Well now, what do we have here?" I rhetorically asked Gina. "Could it be this easy? Really?" Gina set the camera down on the seat and said "I'll be back."

"Wait a minute, what are you going to do?" I asked, not a fan of improvisation on cases, despite being guilty of it myself.

"I don't know yet, but I'll be good, I promise! Don't forget, the judge has never seen me. He doesn't know me at all, just you."

Before I could register any further objections, Gina was already half way to the house.

Marvelous, I thought to myself. I watched as Gina approached the front door and spoke to the woman who answered. Seconds later, Gina disappeared inside the house. I grabbed the camera and took a few pictures as Gina entered the house.

About five long minutes later, I watched as Gina exited the front door and walked along the sidewalk in the opposite direction, away from my car. I pulled away from my parked position and traveled down a parallel street in the same direction that Gina was walking. I picked her up a block away from the residence, well out of their sight.

"Talk to me, Gina. What did you do? What did you find out?" I asked as she was settling in the passenger seat with the grin of a Cheshire cat.

"Buy me lunch and I'll tell you all about it. Then you can go back to the office and call Aetna and tell them to deny the claim," she said.

"Fair enough. How about Italian?"

"I'm game."

We stopped at Mama Rosa's, one of the finer Italian restaurants in Lakewood, and a popular place with the businessmen working downtown. Before exiting the car, Gina grabbed the camera and rewound the film, and handed me the roll with her instructions to get the film developed. She also handed me two dimes and a nickel.

"What's the change for?" I asked.

"Call her. Call her at home and quit acting so sulky. Use the pay phone inside. You're starting to make *me* depressed. Tell her that you're concerned about her son. If you don't, I will!"

Right after we were seated, I excused myself and walked to the bank of three pay phones near the rest rooms at the back of the restaurant.

Choosing the phone on the end, I inserted the coins and called Deana's home number. She picked up the phone after three long rings.

"Hey, how's everything, are you alright? How's your son?" I asked before giving her the chance to answer.

"Marc, I'm sorry about today. Everything is fine, he's got a little bit of a fever, but he'll be alright. I'm really glad you called. It's great to hear from you."

I hung on those words. We spoke for about ten minutes, talking about her son and our missed opportunity for lunch. She promised to make it up next week, and I promised to check back in later to see how things are going.

"I'm holding you to that, you know," Deana said softly. We ended the conversation after a recording came over the phone, demanding that I insert more money if I wanted to continue the call. I assured her that I would check with her later and gently hung up the receiver.

"Better now, Romeo?" asked Gina as I joined her at our table.

"Yeah, I guess. Thanks, Gina." Silence hung in the air until we each ordered from the menu.

❖ ❖ ❖

Back at the office, Gina joined me as we conferred on the case of the federal judge. "He's never going to know what hit him," Gina said, fashioning a smile. "We've got him cold on filing a fraudulent claim and adultery, with adultery being the key part of this case."

Gina formally dictated her notes into the microphone connected to a cassette recorder for later transcription.

Her account was a cleaned-up version of what she relayed to me over lunch, although with the benefit of additional investigation to identify all of the involved parties. It was determined that this well-known federal judge, depicted in the media and accepted in the community as a family man of impeccable moral character, is keeping a concubine, a woman 15 years his junior, identified as Patricia Guajardo. It was also learned that Guajardo gave birth to his child last Christmas.

Under the pretext of purchasing the house next to Guajardo's that is listed for sale, Gina talked her way in to Patricia's house to ask her about a basement flooding issue that she believed the real estate agent was hiding from her.

Using her charm and quick thinking, Gina was able to convincingly disarm the judge's side dish that they would soon be neighbors if the flooding problem proved to be a non-issue.

Assured that the property and her neighborhood is not prone to flooding, Patricia seemed to welcome having an unmarried mother as a potential neighbor.

They all but exchanged recipes for chocolate chip cookies during their brief visit, while the judge was in her bedroom preparing himself for his lunch date. To top it all off, this young woman was wearing a diamond necklace and matching diamond bracelet, which were listed on the police report and insurance claim as being reported stolen. Oh what a tangled web we weave...

At 4:15 p.m., I contacted Paige Vetter, the Aetna claims adjuster, and relayed the whole sordid story. Amid gasps and chuckles coming from Ms. Vetter, she thanked me for our handling of this claim and promised to provide our company with more business. I assured her that she would have the completed report on her desk by the following Monday. In return, she assured me that the judge would be getting a call from her, denying the claim. As far as the theft of the car was concerned, the adjuster said that she would deny the whole claim and let the police sort out the particulars. Case closed, at least for now.

After hanging up the phone, I asked Gina how she thought the federal judge would react upon hearing that he and his 'private' life had just been exposed. "Well, I'm sure glad that he's got *your* business card and not mine," Gina laughed. "You just keep making new friends everywhere you go!"

As her words resonated, I reached over and patted the left side of my suit coat, making sure my gun was still in place. "That reminds me, Gina, I've got to get to the range. Wanna go with me, maybe tomorrow?" I asked.

"Sure, but promise me that one day soon you're gonna get a real gun, Marc."

Satisfied by our good work and good fortune, I left the office early with Gina. We went our separate ways, with Gina going home to her daughter and me going to the Towne Bar to consider the events of the day over a few drinks. Again, Brenda had me all fixed up before I made it to my usual seat at the bar.

I watched the sun set from my barstool, confiding to Brenda my thoughts and hopes. She responded with some of hers. I left the bar just after 9:00 p.m., arriving at my dark, empty apartment with my rented couch. Sitting down and still fully dressed, I turned on the television and quickly drifted into a deep but fitful sleep.

CHAPTER 5

Saturday, May 2, 1987

I awoke on the couch at 3:45 a.m. with a pounding headache and the all-too familiar cotton mouth, the result of drinking my dinner the previous evening. I walked to the kitchen and grabbed a handful of aspirin, settling on four and putting the rest back in the bottle. Against the backdrop of the darkness outside, I saw rain streaming down the kitchen window. Another beautiful day in paradise, I thought.

Instead of going back to bed, I undressed and jumped into the shower, trying to find myself in the hot stream of water beating against the back of my neck. I mentally struggled to identify what day it was, and began replaying the events of yesterday in my mind. I caught myself chuckling about the judge's problems, wondering where he might be sleeping right now.

I thought about Deana, and began feeling sorry for myself over what I missed out yesterday. With a start, I realized that the newspaper article was scheduled for publication today in *The Lakewood Daily Press.* The newspaper had recently changed from publishing a morning and evening edition to a single edition which is usually available about six o'clock each morning.

I jumped from the shower and grabbed my watch from the back of the sink, checking the time. It was only 4:20 a.m., but I wanted to be sure to get ahead of whatever that report might bring.

Since deciding to carry my gun in a shoulder holster, I also decided to dress in either a suit or sport coat to hide my protection.

I changed into my jeans, a dress shirt and a herringbone sport coat, a combination that gave me a semi-professional appearance while keeping my gun out of view.

After completing my morning routine and feeling clean and fresh for the day ahead, I made a pot of coffee to help my mental acuity, and sat at the kitchen table and turned on the overhead light. The light from the kitchen cast an interesting array of shadows into the adjacent living room from the few items of furniture I had managed to borrow from the few friends I had. A couch, a ten-year-old television with rabbit ears and a circular antenna, a wooden coffee table that had seen better days, another table with a lamp that worked most of the time, and a chair covered in orange fabric that was threadbare in spots. Well, at least I had my dignity, I thought to myself.

My headache was letting up, and I was feeling pretty good by the time I finished my second cup of coffee. I walked into the living room to retrieve my briefcase, which was right where I left it the night before. I brought it to the over-sized metal dining table that took a large portion of space in the sparsely furnished kitchen, placed it on the table and after opening it, grabbed the folder containing the notes from our investigation of my uncle's murder. I was a bit surprised not to see my gun in its usual place on top of the folders, but soon realized that it was securely tucked in my shoulder holster under my coat. There, in the stillness of the early morning and by the sound of light rain striking the window, I carefully spread the notes over the table.

The feeling that there was something amiss continued to cling to me. I was unable to shake it. Even worse, I could not figure out what it was.

I reached over to the radio on the counter top and turned it on. The station was present to a FM station, one of the few stations that came in with any degree of clarity. I was surprised the radio worked at all, given its age.

As I made another pot of coffee, the song *Manic Monday* by the all-girl band the Bangles seemed to bounce off the walls of the kitchen, prompting me to reach for the off button. Before I could, however, the radio station went to news, with the FM newscaster rattling off today's top stories. I thought I felt my heart skip a beat when the top story was news of a "possible break" in the five-year-old murder of a schoolteacher, according to a local private detective agency. "Stay tuned for more news at 6:00 a.m." instructed the newscaster.

Wait— what? Did I just hear that correctly? I shook my head rapidly, feeling the coffee rise in the back of my throat and nausea sweeping over me like the rush of a tsunami. Is there some other private investigative agency working on my uncle's case? I sure hope so, because we've got nothing. Zero. Less than zero, in fact. It's 5:15 a.m., and apparently I've got to wait another 45 minutes to learn what I'm apparently already supposed to know.

I stood frozen in the kitchen, holding my coffee cup and wondering what I should do next. Mary Clayburn was certainly long gone from the paper for the night, which is always the source for the radio news broadcasts. What in the world did she write? As it was still too early to get a newspaper anywhere, I decided to wait until the top of the hour to learn what was going on with my investigation. I sat back down and let Cyndi Lauper sing about *True Colors* and laughed as Lionel Ritchie sang *Dancing on the Ceiling,* which is what I was about to do.

Right at 6:00 a.m., the news came on. I listened intently as the newscaster talked about the still unsolved murder of my uncle, and how a private detective agency has new leads in the case. I listened as the newscaster told me that I planned to travel to Miami to follow up new leads on the case. I listened as he described the new leads as "promising," and referenced the story in the *Lakewood Daily Press.* The news abruptly ended and the disc jockey's recap of the day's weather gave way to yet another appropriate song, *The Heat Is On.* Oh, the irony, for indeed it is.

I left my apartment for the closest convenience store, where I bought two copies of today's paper. Placing fifty cents on the counter for the two papers, I walked from the store quickly and drove back to my apartment. Once inside, I opened the paper to the front local section. And there it was, above the fold and in bold type, "Private Detectives Have New Leads In Cold Case Murder."

I could barely believe what I was reading. And hearing again, as the FM broadcast the news again. "Please, make it stop," I found myself muttering. I gathered my notes, the file and newspapers and drove directly to my office, arriving before 7:00 on this gloomy and rainy Saturday morning.

Apparently, I have to get ready to make a trip to Miami, Florida *and* find some promising leads while I'm at it.

❖ ❖ ❖

At 7:15 a.m., I called Paul at his house, rousing him from his slumber. "Hey Paul, what the hell?" I asked.

"What? Why are you calling me so early? What the hell is going on?"

"That's what I want to know. Have you seen the paper yet?"

"What time is it?"

"Quarter after seven. Have you seen the paper, Paul?" I asked.

"What are you talking about, Marc? Go back to bed."

"Okay, I get it. You're not a morning person, but we've got one huge problem Paul. You better get down to the office now," I insisted.

"What time did you say it was?"

"Seven-fifteen. Paul, I'm absolutely serious, you need to get down here because we're gonna have a bunch of news people wanting to know what we know. Or you know. Or what somebody knows, because it sure isn't me, Paul. Not to mention the Lakewood Police wondering the same thing. Oh, and don't forget the D.A.'s office. I'm sure they're going to be quite interested, too. I got nothing, Paul. Nothing. What did you say to Mary that I'm not aware of? Did you talk to her without me?"

"Marc, relax. Go back to bed. I'm sure everything is going to be alright," Paul groggily replied.

At that precise moment, I let loose on Paul. I explained how I was going to go to his house and pull him from his bed. I told him of the unspeakable things I wanted to do to him. I kicked the file cabinet so hard that the stack of files I placed there yesterday went flying into the wall.

"Okay, okay, Marc, calm down, I'll be down after I shower and get dressed,"

"Well thank you," I said it in a way that I'm sure was not lost on Paul.

After I hung up the phone, I kicked the file cabinet again for good measure. I decided not to take the phones off of the answering service. I was afraid at what calls might come in, and I certainly did not want to talk to anyone.

Even with the phones being handled by an answering service, they still ring inside the office. An intricate reel-to-reel taping system also captures the conversation with the service, a system set up by a 'government technician' who now works for the telephone company and is Paul's brother-in-law. The incessant ringing began at 7:50 a.m.

It was now 8:15 and the phones are still ringing. Paul is still AWOL, and I am plagued by a near constant beeping noise coming from somewhere in my office. It took me a while to locate the beeping sound. It was coming from my desk drawer, or more specifically, the pager in the top drawer of my desk. It took me another minute to realize that it must be Paul trying to reach me, as the phones are still being answered by the service.

I called Paul and he answered. "Where are you?" I asked.

"I saw the paper and just wanted you to know that I'll be over shortly," said Paul.

"Really? That's what you called to tell me?" By now my frustration level was off the charts. I slammed the phone down as I heard him say "relax!"

❖ ❖ ❖

It was almost 11:00 a.m. when the door to the front office flew open. I was surprised to see Gina and not Paul walk through the door. "Marc, what in the hell is going on? Do you realize what's all over the news? What's the break we've got?" she asked.

"Gina, I'm hoping that you can tell me."

The look that came over her said everything. She slumped against the door and asked if Paul was here.

"Nope, it's just you and me. I called Paul and he was supposed to be here hours ago. The phone has been ringing off the hook."

"Oh, this can't be good."

"Tell me about it."

Just then, Paul walked through the door. Both Gina and I shot him a glance that could kill.

"What?" he said with a wry smile.

Gina started, "Paul, in the name of everything that's holy tell us right now what's going on. You better start talking right freakin' now." It was at this point in time that I realized that it was probably not a good idea to get Gina riled up, as she began to scare even me by her posture. As Paul walked into his office, I really thought Gina was going to jump on his back— I mean literally. There was no way I was going to get between them, I thought.

Paul sat behind his desk with Gina just inches from his head. "Start talking, Paul. Because it sure seems like you threw Marc and me to the wolves. You better have a really good explanation, or better yet, a suspect."

"Both of you, just relax."

"Paul, if you tell me to relax one more time—" Paul cut me off mid-sentence.

"Here's the deal." I called Mary Clayburn after the interview and said that we do have a suspect, or somebody in our sights."

"Good, Paul, then perhaps you can tell me who. I'm sure a lot of people right now want to know. I'm sure my family for one. Oh, wait, yeah, I'd like to know too. Yeah, for sure. And the police, I'm sure, and the D.A.'s office. So, just who is this mystery man, anyway? You just come waltzing into the office now, hours after I called you, Paul, *hours*."

"Would you two just shut up for a minute and give me a chance to explain?" Paul pleaded. "The way I see it, we need a break. To get a break, we need people to start getting nervous." He continued.

"We need people to start talking, thinking that we know more than we do. So I dropped a few hints to Mary after the interview. I figure we'll be getting some feedback from some people."

"Really Paul, that's your plan? Please tell me there's more, Paul," I heard myself screaming at him. By this time, I was sweating profusely. Gina was pacing back and forth in the office.

"What, you don't like my plan?" Paul asked with a smirk.

"I don't believe it, Paul," Gina said.

"And I'm not talking to the press, or anyone for that matter. You call my family, because I'm sure they are going to want to know the inside story on this wonderful plan of yours," I said.

"I'll handle everything," Paul responded. Now, the two of you better start packing your bags, because I'm sending you both down to Miami."

"Well, here's a newsflash for you, Paul. I need at least a week's notice, Paul. I mean, I've got a daughter I've got to look out for," Gina said.

"Fine, you two can leave a week from this Monday. That's the eleventh. That should give you both ample time to calm down."

"Don't count on it," Gina shot back.

"Marc, start carrying your beeper with you from now on."

"Kiss my ass, Paul." I turned and walked into my office, followed by Gina. She sat in the chair in front of my desk while I called our answering service for messages. Unsurprisingly, we had a lot.

Three were requests from the local television stations for on-camera interviews, two messages were from a cranky sounding Detective McCarty of the Lakewood Police Department, or at least that's what the answering service operator said, one from Mary Clayburn, five from different members of my family, twelve from people who claimed to have information about the case, and one from Deana. I kept the message from Deana, slid the so-called tips to Gina, and dropped the remaining pile onto Paul's desk without saying a word.

"So, how many did we get?"

"How many of what, Paul?"

"Leads. Tips. You know, people who called about the case? If you are going to keep them to yourself, Marc, I suggest you check them out thoroughly," Paul said.

Hoarse, tired and frustrated, I stopped and stared at him. "Good plan, Paul."

"By the way, you can expect more as news gets around," Paul added.

"Marvelous. Just marvelous."

I walked back into my office, slamming the door behind me. As I sat down behind my desk, Gina spoke up. "Marc, you might want to take a look at one of these tips you took a little closer. Look at the name." The tip was from Benjamin Cooper, the guy who visited my uncle the night he was murdered. Apparently, he had more to say—much more.

Even though I wrote it myself, I was so angry that my emotions apparently muted the intellectual part of my brain. "Maybe Paul hasn't lost his mind entirely."

As I stared at the name, I instinctively placed my right hand on my gun, making sure it was with me. From the corner of my eye, I caught Gina checking her purse for her gun as well.

Gina and I spent the remainder of the afternoon alone in the office, relentlessly pouring over all of the notes from the previous days in light of this new tip we received from Mr. Cooper. Gina called him at 3:15 p.m., although he said he couldn't talk right then. He was at home with his family, and preferred to talk to us on Monday after he finished some business and out of earshot of his wife. He assured us that it would worth our time.

After Gina left, I tried to return Deana's call, but there was no answer. I tried two more times before I left the office without success. Despondent but far from surprised, I figured that I would call her on Monday.

❖ ❖ ❖

It was 7:45 when I finished my gourmet meal of a Big Mac and fries from McDonald's. I decided to stop at the Towne Bar for my usual. To my surprise, Brenda was working the weekend and had already set up me again before I even made it to my seat. "Hey 'Mr. Celebrity,'" she said as I sat down. "That's all I've been hearing, all day, is the news about the murder case," she added. When I responded with a grumble, she asked me what was wrong in light of the big developments. I just shook my head and responded with the phrase I began using more frequently of late. "You just don't want to know."

I stayed for only an hour. As I was leaving, Brenda grabbed my arm and pulled me toward her, whispering "Be careful" in my ear. Silently, I wondered whether she knew something I didn't. The way I felt, everybody knew more than me at this point. It's not a good feeling at all.

CHAPTER 6

Monday, May 4, 1987

I arrived at my office at 8:15 a.m. Annie and Gina were already there and heavily into the coffee by the time I arrived. I grabbed a cup and walked into my office, breaking my mundane but ceremonial task of removing my gun from my briefcase or opening it at all. Gina followed me into my office and asked if I had anything more to report from the fallout Saturday. I was still angry at Paul for his recklessness with the facts, although both me and Gina calmed considerably since Saturday.

"Nothing," I said. "Paul talked to my family and put the cops and D.A. off until today."

Gina sat down in front of my desk, looking exhausted.

"You okay, Gina," I asked?

"Fine. Just some things at home. Not the greatest."

"Anything I can do to help?"

"Yeah, take me to Disneyland. I'm ready for a road trip. So Romeo, were you able to talk to Deana?"

"No, not since last week," I said. "I'm ready for a road trip myself, but I don't think Disneyland is in the cards."

We made plans to contact Benjamin Cooper at his place of business, deciding that it would be best to have Gina make the call again and arrange the interview. Since she called him on Saturday, we reasoned that he might feel more comfortable with the continuity. At 9:20, Gina called Benjamin Cooper at his jewelry store business. It took about two minutes, but Cooper finally came to the phone.

"Mr. Cooper, this is Gina Russell calling back. We spoke briefly on Saturday, remember? What time can you come to our office today," asked Gina, giving Cooper little room to maneuver.

What Gina perceived as friendliness on Saturday changed to a much chillier reception today. Something changed over the last 36 hours, and not for the better.

"I don't want to meet at your office, and I certainly don't want you guys here. You guys are 'too hot' right now and I don't want us to be seen together. I'll meet you at the dock at 4:00. Come alone, Ms. Russell. No cops, no one else. Understand?"

I was listening on an extension in the office. Cooper's demands sounded like something from a cheesy television detective show. Also, Gina did not like to have suspects or informants dictate the location or conditions of meetings, and didn't particularly like Cooper's attitude and expressed her displeasure to Cooper.

"You called us, remember?" said Gina, standing her ground.

"Just be there if you want to hear what I've got to say. I'll be in a red 1986 Mustang T-Top parked on the west side of the dock right at 4:00." There was a click and the line went dead.

"What do you think? asked Gina.

"I think the guy likes nice red cars. Oh, and I think I'm going with you."

"No, Marc, you heard him. he might not talk if you're there."

"Baloney, Gina. You're not going alone."

After several minutes of verbal wrangling, we finally settled on a plan that was agreeable to both of us. I would go to the dock at noon in a conversion van that we occasionally borrowed for long-term surveillance assignments or when our vehicles were 'burned.' That would give me a full four hours to watch the area, making sure that the meeting was not some sort of set-up. Well, at least doing whatever I could to make certain, if that was even possible. At least I would cover Gina during the meeting.

We also instructed Richard Dunlap, one of our investigators free at the time, to loosely tail Cooper from his business to the dock to make sure he was coming alone.

Several minutes later, Paul arrived at the office. Gina advised him of the arrangements she made with Cooper, and I filled him in on the backup plan.

"Sounds good," Paul said to both of us. "But make sure you both wear your beepers in case I need to contact you." I had all but forgotten about the obnoxious little box that was still in my desk drawer.

"Fine," I replied to Paul.

"Marc, take the Mossberg. Keep it in the van just in case," Paul cautioned.

Paul was talking about the Mossberg 500, a .12-gauge shotgun that is known as a special purpose model shotgun with an adjustable stock. It is quite intimidating, especially if you are on the wrong side of it. Paul kept it in the office for such 'special purposes.'

"No argument there, Paul."

Shortly after making our plans, I picked up the conversion van at the house of one of Paul's friends who lived only a few blocks from our office. His friend was at work, but called his wife to let her know that I would be stopping by to borrow the vehicle for the day.

As I inspected the interior to make sure it would be suitable for the assignment while the owner's wife stood by with the keys, I found a small, stuffed, fuzzy brown bear with a red ribbon around its neck, tied in a bow and wedged in the crease of the back bench seat. Based on its appearance, sporting a few old stains on its light jacket and the bit of stuffing protruding from its left ear, it was well worn. No, it was well loved by its owner.

The sight of the bear stopped me cold as I considered the contrast. The bear that belonged to some sweet, innocent little girl was about to be replaced by a .12-gauge shotgun. At that moment as I was crouched inside the van holding the bear, I was overcome by a flood of emotions. I thought about my own kids, about Deana, and about life in general. I was brought back to reality by the woman outside who asked me if everything was okay.

"Fine," I said, exchanging the stuffed animal for the keys with a forced smile. "I'm sure somebody will be looking for this," handing the small treasured object to the woman.

"Oh gee, thank you! My Emily would be upset if she lost this little guy," she said. She handed me the keys and I left, still musing about the contrasts in life.

Before leaving the office, I called Deana at her office, relieved that she picked up the phone after only one ring. This was the first time I had talked to her since last week and before the article appeared in the paper.

"Hey, I was worried about you. I read the article in the paper. What's going on? Are you alright?" she asked.

"Me? I'm fine. I was worried about you, especially since I couldn't reach you on Saturday. Are you okay? How's your son?" I asked.

"He's fine and I'm fine. It's you I'm concerned about. I didn't know you guys were closing in on somebody."

"Yeah, well, neither did I. It's a long story, and I'm sure you're too busy to hear about it now. Do you still feel like having lunch again sometime?"

"Wow. Lunch with a celebrity. I don't know if my heart could take it! I'd love it, though, whenever you have a chance to break free."

I told her about our plans to travel to Florida next week, and expressed my desire to see her at least once before I left. We planned to meet for lunch on Thursday, the only day she had free as her schedule was as punishing as mine. Before we ended the call, she said, "Whatever you're doing, please be careful. I'd like to keep you around for a while." Her concern warmed my heart and made me smile, which is something I hadn't done in the last few days.

❖ ❖ ❖

I was in position at the dock at precisely 12:00 noon. From my vantage position, I could see all vehicles entering the dock area, and took an inventory of the vehicles present and parked at the dock's edge. I had everything I needed, including a thermos of coffee, a fresh pack of Marlboros, a 35 mm camera as well as a video camera, the shotgun, my .38, and, of course, my beeper. I settled in the rear of the van for the long wait.

I watched Gina arrive at 3:45, visibly alone as the driver of her car. She parked toward the end of the dock, backing into a space so she would be facing forward. A good position, I thought, in the event she had to exit quickly and one that provided me with a favorable vantage point. At 3:58, Bruce Cooper arrived, driving his red Mustang just as he stated. He appeared to be alone and pulled his car up next to Gina. I watched him exit and walk to the passenger side of Gina's car. After a few seconds of conversation, I saw Gina reach over to unlock the passenger door. Cooper sat in the passenger seat. Whatever Cooper was saying must have been important, as I watched Gina write feverishly on a legal pad.

The entire meeting lasted 20 minutes, according to my watch. Cooper exited Gina's car and entered his, hastily leaving the dock without giving me or anyone else a second look. Gina allowed him time to depart the area and then left, traveling in the direction back to our office. By the time I arrived, it was 4:45. Gina was already seated in my office, still writing on her legal pad. Four pages of bright yellow paper were covered by black ink.

"So, how did it go?" I asked.

"Marc, sit down, you're not going to believe what I have."

For the next 45 minutes, Gina recounted her conversation with Cooper. According to Cooper, my uncle had a photo album containing Polaroid photos of numerous males in various sexual positions with other men. The album itself was narrow in width and had a type of cross on the cover. He called it an Ankh, which is some sort of satanic or demonic symbol. Your uncle also had an assortment of loose pictures that were also Polaroid photos. Hours before Jerry was stabbed to death, he met Cooper at the bookstore. They were both regular patrons and knew each other, but had not talked to each other since they were in the army together. Cooper said that they had no previous direct contact with each other until that night when Jerry invited Cooper to his house to view his photo collection.

"Well, Gina, as I see it, then, either he was lying five years ago, or he is lying now."

"Don't be so quick to judge, Marc. It's deeper than that. What motive would he have to lie to me or to us now? I can almost understand why he lied or kept things from the police. He was concerned at what he saw. He said he saw the activity shown in those pictures when he was in black ops in the military, the same program as your uncle.

He *already knew* the sinister nature of what he was looking at. He recognized at least one of the men in the album. He identified a man who appeared in several photographs as an assistant district attorney right here in Lakewood. A guy who works closely with the cops."

"Go on."

"Jerry told him that there were some other pictures of very

prominent and well respected people, so-called pillars of the community, recognizable names and faces, having sex with each other, sex orgies and in some cases, sex acts with young boys. All in living color. Other pictures were of young boys who seemed to be part of some ritualistic, sadomasochistic parties. Some of the younger males were bound, gagged and appeared to have been beaten. Pretty intense stuff."

"My uncle was a part of this? I don't believe it, Gina," I said.

"Part of it? No, not quite, not exactly, Marc. According to Cooper, Jerry told him that he was given the album by somebody out of state, someone from Florida. Jerry told Cooper that there's a large underground market for pictures that are not 'officially' sold at your local porn shops. Believe it or not, some guys pay big money for such pictures. Others, I think, based on what Cooper told me, use them for blackmail. Or even other reasons we don't even know about yet."

"Wait, are you now telling me that my uncle was engaged in blackmailing others? And this album, coming from another state had photos of locals? How does that work?"

"Now you're getting ahead of me. First, I not saying that your uncle was involved in blackmail. I'm not sure that Cooper himself is certain there was simply one album, but he only saw one album as well as other loose photos. The album and photos were in the top center dresser drawer, the same drawer that was empty. The drawer with blood transfer stains."

"Okay, continue."

"When Cooper met your uncle that night, Jerry was pretty wasted. He probably said more than he should have. Do you remember what you told me after our big meeting last week that you envisioned something from the movie *Looking For Mr. Goodbar* when Paul was giving us all of the details? Well, that's your uncle!" Gina exclaimed. "Or at least that was him that night. He made advances to Jerry."

"Okay, I get that. But where do these pictures come in to play. My uncle wasn't part of that, isn't that what you're saying?"

"Listen to me. I'm not saying that either. I don't know yet, Marc. I don't think he was, but what I am sure of is that he was the male version of Diane Keaton's character in the movie, just like you thought and just like you mentioned to me after the briefing."

"I still don't understand."

"Look, Marc, this is new information from just one meeting with one person. We don't have all of the facts yet. We don't know all of the details. There's a lot more to figure out here. But what I do know is that we've apparently stumbled into something much larger than a simple murder, not that murder is simple. *But there's something much bigger here.* We're talking about pedophilia, sadomasochism, parties or orgies involving men and underage boys, all of it unthinkable. Exactly how all of this relates to your uncle, or just how deeply he was involved, remains to be seen. There's one more thing, Marc."

"What's that?"

"Cooper was in the army at the same time Jerry was. Involved in the same programs, based on his own admissions from what Cooper thought was just casual, ice-breaking conversation."

It took several minutes for me to grasp the magnitude of what Gina just conveyed to me. I finally understood the obvious during the short but uncomfortable silence that followed her summation of the meeting.

"So where are the pictures? Where's the album that Cooper reportedly saw? There was nothing in the police report that listed any such property, and I certainly didn't see it during my inspection of Jerry's bedroom before the police arrived."

"Like I said, Cooper said that your uncle removed it from the top drawer of his dresser," Gina replied." It was not inventoried by the police. It's whereabouts, along with the assorted loose Polaroids is the sixty-four-thousand-dollar question."

"Do we know for certain that there are recognizable faces in that album and the other pictures? Can we be certain that the young men were underage?"

"Well, again, Cooper seemed genuinely curious, even worried by what he saw. I suspect that's the reason he said that be returned to your uncle's house later that night. Long story short, Cooper wanted a second look at the album to see if there was anybody he knew, or that's his version. He confessed to me that he thought of taking the photos, stealing them outright, maybe to blackmail some people himself, especially if he knew them to be guys with money or stature in the community."

"Nice guy," I said. "So what happened when Cooper went back to my uncle's house around 11:00 that night?" I asked.

"According to Cooper, Jerry wasn't there. He parked his car in front of your uncle's house, walked to the back door and rang the bell. After ringing the bell and knocking a few times, he left. This also fits with what the neighbor reported," Gina said. "After that, Cooper went home to his wife, arriving at his house before midnight, which matches exactly what his wife told the police."

I sat silently, dazed and confused at what I was hearing.

After listening to this update, I left the office to remove all of the equipment from the van. I drove it back to its owner, thanking him and his wife for allowing us to use it. As he stood on the driveway, his little girl was standing on his left foot, hugging his leg and using it as a makeshift pole. "Daddy, can we go get some ice cream now? Please?" she asked, looking up to her father with a pouty but adorable face. After saying please a few more times, her father relented and instructed her to get her mother so they could all go together. My heart ached for my own little daughter who I hadn't seen in well over a week.

Instead of going directly back to the office, I took a side trip to the Towne Bar for quiet reflection and to treat my 'heart problems' with copious doses of medicinal bourbon. I changed my mind about the purpose of my visit, and instead used the pay phone on the wall next to rest rooms to call the office. Gina answered, and I asked her to join me for an extended review of the case. As Gina's mother was taking care of her only granddaughter for the night, Gina agreed and showed up ten minutes later. I had already commissioned a table at the far end of the bar, next to a floor-to-ceiling window that provided an unobstructed view of the bar's parking lot and outside tables. I was on my second glass of bourbon and had a beer waiting for her before she sat down.

For the first few rounds, we each took turns talking about our personal problems, finding a lot of common ground between us. Gina listened graciously and patiently as I poured my heart out to her about my estrangement or self-imposed exile from my family, my lack of a real home, and most of all, the growing intensity of my feelings toward Deana. She, in turn provided insight into her personal situation, facilitated by cheap well drinks during 'happy hour.'

We wondered aloud about the origins of 'happy hour' as it seemed to fall far short of its otherwise promising name. We wondered about what we had gotten ourselves into, feeling that somehow we were poking at a very large bear, and that bear was awakened and about to become very angry at our actions.

Perhaps it was due to the feelings stirred by our talk of the case that I urged Gina, in a voice just above a whisper, to casually look out the window to her left. I cautioned her to act normally and not to stare, but to simply look at a particular vehicle parked in a second row of cars in the parking lot. There is a man seated in the driver's seat of a non-descript vehicle, appearing to be waiting for someone.

There are three things in life that I know, without any doubt whatsoever, that I'm very good at. Spotting surveillance is one of them. She glanced outside and looked back at me.

"Gina, do you see what I see?"

"Yes I do."

"Is he a friend of yours, perhaps?" I asked.

"Nope. How long has he been there?"

"I noticed him when I sat down. I saw him pull out of one parking space closer to the front of the bar to where he's at now. He was here before you arrived."

We decided to keep an eye on him while we finished our informal meeting. We stopped dulling our senses through the process of self-medication, and switched to soft drinks. We also drew up a general action plan for the next few days in light of the information Gina obtained today and the 'leads and tips' that continued to flow into our office, generated by the newspaper article and news reports over the weekend.

Gina mentioned that Annie put a small stack of new messages on my desk before leaving for the day. As the evening was still early, we decided to go back to the office to see what nuggets we might find and to see if our new friend might follow us.

Our server brought our tab which came to a grand total of $12.20, thanks to the discounts of happy hour. I left a twenty on the table and we both drove back to the office in a manner we settled upon before we even left our seats. Gina pulled out of the parking lot first and I followed, as did the third, uninvited member of our mobile entourage.

Gina turned onto the lot in front of our office while I made a right-hand turn into the plaza across the street. I watched as the unidentified male, driving a gray Ford sedan proceeded straight. My plan was to make an immediate U-turn out of the lot and get behind the mystery man to record the plate number of the car. The plan would have worked flawlessly had it not been for the older woman in a large Lincoln who was blocking the plaza's exit. She seemed to be exercising extreme caution as she inched her boat onto the road to turn left. Apparently, my actions of first beeping my horn, followed by a flurry of expletives and animated hand motions only made matters worse. Upon hearing the sound of my horn, the older woman stepped on her breaks, bringing her vehicle to a complete stop half in and half out of the lot.

By the time I was able to extricate myself from the position between her car and the pick-up that had already assumed his position behind me, I lost visual contact with the mystery car. As I quickly turned onto the road in an attempt to catch up to the Ford, it had disappeared. Stopping on the side of the road about a mile from my office, I pounded the steering wheel out of frustration and let loose another stream of verbal assaults. My actions must have looked pretty strange to the middle-aged couple walking their dog on the sidewalk.

They looked at me curiously as they walked by my passenger side door. I returned to the office and updated Gina.

Among the stack of telephone messages written by Annie were a several 'tips' by blatant crackpots and people who had obviously just too much time on their hands, two more requests by the local television media for interviews, a message from a psychic who claimed to know the identity of the killer, and two messages that appeared legitimate if not promising.

Of the two more promising messages, one was from a young man who claimed to have been a student of my uncle, and another from a man who provided just the right amount of information that contained certain keywords and even names that elevated its importance above the others. That message also included a reference to people in Florida, suggesting that this person has knowledge that was never made public. I put those aside to be addressed in the morning. Gina mentioned that the timing of our upcoming Florida trip seemed serendipitous, and I agreed.

I grabbed my briefcase and made sure my gun was secured in my shoulder holster as we both left the office for the night, headed for our respective locations we each call 'home.'

CHAPTER 7

Tuesday, May 5, 1987

I left my apartment at 6:15 a.m. after a fitful night's sleep. After first buying a cup of coffee at McDonald's, I drove around for several minutes to see if anyone was following me. As I arrived at my office without seeing anyone except a few early morning joggers, two dog walkers, and a team of trash collectors, the thought crossed my mind that I was being paranoid, and the events of the day before were the products of a tired and overactive imagination.

I spent the first few hours of my day reviewing several new assignments we received from Aetna, and Nabb's Trucking company. One assignment from Aetna was from their board of directors. They selected a candidate to head their financial services division, and it was our job to find any skeletons in his closet. Because of the position, and the access he would have to their financial accounts, we would not only be looking for skeletons, but also for skeleton dust. The assignment from Nabb's involved the apparent theft of Tandy computers from their loading docks, or somewhere within their warehouse.

After sorting through the new cases and assigning the preliminary investigation of each case to Richard, Gary and Gina, I turned my attention to my uncle's murder. I hung my new cork board on the wall next to the older one that was completely covered by index cards and yarn. I moved several cards from the old board to the new, and added several more cards as well. I also pinned the telephone messages we received the day before to the new cork board, and used a blue marker to make a star on the two more promising messages.

I heard Annie walk into the outer office just before 8:00 a.m., followed by Gina seconds later. I called Gina into my office and asked if anyone had accompanied her as she drove to the office. Nothing. No signs of any mobile surveillance, and no indication of any surveillance of our office at this early hour.

Second guessing myself about the events of the previous evening, I suggested to Gina that perhaps we were just being paranoid. "I'd like to think so, too," was her reply.

We discussed the two leads that came in, noting that both were received late in the afternoon. We decided to wait until later in the day to make the calls, and used a 1986-1987 crisscross directory of phone numbers that Paul had purchased earlier that year, in an attempt to put a name to each number. One telephone number was identified as a residential land-line, but "xxxx" appeared where the address and name would normally appear in the directory. "I knew it couldn't be that easy," I told Gina. The other number was listed to the Ruby Slipper Lounge, a bar of dubious repute in Lakewood. We decided to dispense with the paying clients first and attack those messages later in the day.

Before digging into the various mundane tasks of preparing our notes for Annie, who would then polish and type them in a manner suitable for presentation to our clients, Gina moved from her desk in the outer office to a smaller desk in mine. Considering that we would now be working closely on my uncle's murder, the move was logical. The only problem we encountered was our different tastes in background music. While working, I liked soft classical music in the background, while Gina preferred adult contemporary. "Just how old are you anyway, Marc?" was Gina's comment regarding my preference. The joking was respectful, and I pretended that I didn't notice the change of the radio to a more modern station.

As we completed our reports and other paperwork, morning turned to afternoon. At 12:30 p.m., Gina asked me if I was hungry. She offered to order take-out from the diner in the plaza across from our office for her, Annie and me. Considering that this would be my first meal of the day, I ordered two chili dogs and a can of Mountain Dew to wash them down. "Breakfast of champions," muttered Gina. I gave her a five-dollar bill for lunch, and another five, asking her to stop at the convenience store to buy me two more packs of cigarettes. She left the office, intending to stop at the store first.

During Gina's absence, I reached into my briefcase and pulled out the card I received from Deana the previous week. It seemed like a year ago. I read it again, and became lost in thought, lost in the memories of the last time we were together. Even though the span of time was short, it seemed like an eternity since I last saw her in person. I longed to see her again. Picking up the phone, I called her at her office, taking the chance that she might still be at her desk, even though it was lunch time. To my pleasant surprise, she answered.

"Hey, I, hello, I mean, I'm glad I caught you," I said, tripping over my tongue. It was as if the words just fell out of my mouth and into the mouthpiece of the telephone handset.

"Well, this is a nice surprise," responded Deana, politely pretending not to notice my jumbling.

"I was just thinking of you, so I thought I'd give you a call."

"I'm glad you did," she replied. "We're still on for Thursday, aren't we?"

"Absolutely."

"Great. I'm looking forward to it."

We talked for a few more minutes, during which I did my best to subtly suggest that I could be her knight in shining armor, that I was her answer to a future of caring love and stability, despite the unpleasantness she had experienced from the all-too-recent dissolution of her marriage. I did not want to scare her off, so I did my best to keep the conversation light and witty. I tried to "put my best foot forward," as they say, without tripping over it. Although I stumbled throughout the conversation, I was silently hoping that she appreciated my effort. Our conversation concluded after confirming our lunch plans for Thursday.

Ten minutes later, Gina walked into my office carrying a grease laden paper bag containing my lunch. After placing the bag on my desk, she reached into her purse and handed me two packs of Marlboros. Without saying anything, she walked to the door and closed it, and walked back to my desk. Talking barely above a whisper, she leaned over to tell me that the car we saw the night before, the car we thought was following us, was back.

"Where is he now?" I asked.

"Parked in the second row of the plaza parking lot, facing our office. I passed him when I left the diner. He's the only one in the car. He looked to be about 40 or so, white, short brown hair, and dressed in a suit. She pulled a slip of paper from her pocket and handed it to me.

"Here's his plate number."

Paul had been in his office since 9:30 that morning and remained deeply involved in establishing a security company to supplement our investigative agency. Gina asked him to join us in our office to discuss "an important development." A few minutes later, Paul walked in and sat down. We filled him in on the events of the previous evening, and Gina's encounter with the same car that morning. Paul asked for the plate number, stating that he would use his contact at the Lakewood Police Department to determine who owned the vehicle "in real time." Going through the normal process could take up to 24 hours. Considering the situation, we all agreed that this would be the best course of action. I handed the slip of paper, with the plate number hastily scribbled across it, to Paul, who disappeared back in his office.

He returned ten minutes later with a troubled look on his face.

"Are you two sure this is the plate number?" he asked.

"Positive," said Gina. "Why?"

"Because Pete, my contact at the department, ran it twice. Both times it came back as 'no record found.' There's no history of that plate ever being issued, either."

"So what does that mean?" I asked.

"It means that we either have a well-dressed man inside a car with a completely bogus plate, or a plate that is being used for undercover work by the cops, most likely by the feds," said Paul. "Either way, it doesn't sound good."

After a few minutes of discussion, Paul decided to call his contact again for information and advice. Pete promised Paul that he would make a few inquiries and call him back when he learned something. Meanwhile, Pete suggested that we "do not engage" the person until we knew a little bit more, and Paul agreed.

"So we just wait?" I asked.

"That's all you should do right now, until we know who we're dealing with, and find out why this guy has such an interest in you two," he said.

Gina and I ate our lunch in silence, both of us wondering about the mystery man and whoever sent him. The minutes seemed to turn to hours after we finished lunch and continued to work on the mundane, and no answers were forthcoming.

At 3:15 p.m., Paul walked into my office and sat down in a chair between Gina and me.

"So, here's the deal," he said. "Pete called me before leaving for the day. He made some casual inquiries with the chief, and also called a contact he has at the FBI. He said that they both denied any knowledge of the Ford and the guy in it."

"Do you believe him?" asked Gina.

"I believe Pete, but I'm not sure I believe his contacts."

"I'm surprised that no one from the plaza called the police to report a suspicious vehicle in the lot," I said.

"They did," Paul chuckled. "A marked car was dispatched a few hours ago, but when the patrol car arrived, the car and the guy were gone. The patrol cop made a few rounds of the lot and nearby areas, but never found the car."

"Pretty convenient, isn't it?" I said.

"Maybe a little too convenient," said Paul.

"Tipped off?

"Maybe."

"Pete talked to the chief and told him about the situation. He said that the next time either one of you spots the car within Lakewood, get to a pay phone and call it in. He told dispatch to make sure that the call is given a high priority. Even if it's outside of Lakewood, call only them and they will contact the proper agency having jurisdiction."

"How oddly helpful of them," I said.

❖ ❖ ❖

Still troubled by the thought of being under surveillance by someone else, an irony that was not lost on either of us, Gina and I finished the paperwork relating to our closed cases and completed basic telephone inquiries and preliminary investigation on the new cases. At 4:15, Gina said that she would stick around while I called the two most promising leads pinned to the board.

I called the number on what seemed to be the best lead first. A woman answered after the first ring. After I told her who I was, and asked for the person who called, she identified herself as Mary Tingsley, the wife of Martin Tingsley. Her husband was a former student and close friend of my uncle. Although I recognized the Tingsleys from the police department's investigative report, the telephone number was different than the one on file.

She whispered into the phone, "Please, you must talk to my husband. He knows more than he told the police. I just don't want him to know I prompted you to call him." I assured her that her secret was safe with me, and instructed her to put him on the phone. After about a minute of talk, muffled by the placement of her hand over the mouthpiece of the phone, a voice on the other end said, "This is Martin Tingsley."

I introduced myself and told him that we needed to talk. I rustled a few papers so he could hear them on his end of the phone, and told him that I was just looking at the section of the police report that contained his statement. I said that, based on our investigation, he obviously left some things out of his narrative to the police detectives. Seated across from me, Gina shot a frown-turned-confused look at me. In return, I shrugged my shoulders.

I asked when I could come over to see him. Interestingly, he asked when we were planning to leave for Florida. I told him soon, and asked why he wanted to know. He said he needed to talk to me before that, so I suggested that I stop over right now. This game of verbal ping-pong lasted for several more volleys, until he finally asked if he and his wife could come to our office to talk, out of earshot of Martin's mother-in-law, with whom they now lived. She would babysit their little girl while we met. I agreed, and the conversation terminated after I gave him the address of our office.

I related his end of the conversation to Gina. Her interest was piqued.

"You don't mind if I sit in on the interview, do you?" asked Gina.

"Of course not. Maybe we can separate them. You can take Mary, and I'll handle Martin. They'll be here in a few minutes."

At this time, Annie stuck her head in my office and said she was leaving early for a dentist appointment. Paul followed her out, saying that he had some errands to do.

While waiting for the Tingsleys to arrive, I called the number listed on the other message slip. After four rings, a man answered the phone. "Ruby's," he said, over the din of loud background noise of people and music. I asked for Roland, the name that appeared on the message slip.

"He's not here yet. Check back later, after six," said the man, hanging up the phone after delivering me the news.

Mary and Martin Tingsley arrived at our office within fifteen minutes of our conversation, apparently wasting no time after I called. Although Gina did her best to split the two, Martin had a pretty firm grasp on his wife's arm, yet Mary appeared to be fully in charge. After a brief, private consultation with Gina in the outer office, as we excused ourselves to get our respective files, we decided to let them stay together this time. We'd hear them out and decide from there. We returned to my office, each of us carrying a different file folder unrelated to the murder investigation. Gina brought a chair and placed it next to mine behind the desk. Both of us now sat opposite the Tingsleys.

Mary began by saying that she met her husband when he was just 16 years old, which was only six years before, and not quite a year before my uncle's murder. She stated that he was "a mess" when she met him, claiming that he was sexually abused by numerous men on countless occasions, at different times and places, starting a few years before. Mary ultimately "saved him" from this abuse by telling Martin's mother, who then alerted Lakewood detectives, and even the FBI, to the abuse.

I glanced over at Martin and noticed that beads of sweat were developing on his forehead, despite the comfortable temperatures in my office. I offered him a cigarette, which he gladly accepted, despite the scowl he received from his wife. I lit his cigarette and joined him, sharing the ashtray between us. Meanwhile, Mary never missed a beat.

"Martin was sexually abused by some of the most respected men of Lakewood," said Mary, whose words seemed to hang in the air like the stagnant smoke created by our cigarettes. "Is that true, Martin?" asked Gina in a compassionate tone.

"Yes. But you know what, nobody believed me. Not one of the damn investigators believed me, even though I had proof." Martin was now sweating profusely, and his hands were beginning to shake. "Not one of those bastards wanted to believe me, or believed that their friends are a bunch of sexual perverts." Gina reached over and put her hand on Martin's arm. "Take it easy. We'll help you however we can," she said.

"Martin, you said you had proof. What was it?" I asked.

"I brought it with me. In fact, I've got it on me," he said. "I take it everywhere I go." By now, Martin's voice was trembling and he appeared to be on the verge of tears.

"Can I see it, Martin?" I asked in the gentlest tone I could muster.

"Damn right you can see it. I have to look at it every day, so why shouldn't you see it too?"

Martin jumped out of his chair, but never averted his gaze from my eyes. I found that to be particularly disturbing. I instinctively slid my right hand into my coat and grabbed the handle of my revolver, a move not lost on Martin. "Relax," he said. "Just look."

Martin removed his shirt from his waistband and lifted it to just above his nipples. There, on his stomach and upper abdomen, were several scoop-like indentations on his skin. They were randomly patterned, yet appeared to be of the same relative size. Some had irregular edges, while the others were smoother in appearance. Before either Gina or I could say anything, he turned around to show us his back. Another dozen or so marks.

"Are those what I think they are?" I asked incredulously.

"I don't know what you think they are," said Martin, "but I'll tell you exactly what they are. They're cigarette burns, and a few cigar burns as well."

I looked at Mary and saw tears running down her face. By now, Martin was shaking so badly that he could not hold his shirt up any longer. Shocked, Gina was holding her hand over her mouth.

Martin turned around and began to unbuckle his belt.

"What in the hell are you doing?" I asked, as Gina began to squirm in her seat.

"Don't worry, I'm not going to get cute. I just want you to see it all," Martin replied.

Mary spoke up and assured Gina as well. Martin had already dropped his pants to his knees, displaying the same type of circular scars on his upper thighs. He turned around again and pulled the waistband of his shorts down to the crack of his buttocks, revealing a closer grouping of the scars near the top of his rear. A longer, straight scar extended down to the fleshy part of his right cheek, which was partially covered by his underwear.

"See them?" Martin asked. "Do you see them?" he pressed.

I assured Martin I did, telling him that he could get dressed, while Gina expressed her sorrow and concern. By now, his wife was crying, and I was busy looking for tissues to give her. Gina scooped up her purse and gave her a handful.

After Martin was fully buttoned back up and seated, he appeared to be much calmer than before. He then said something I never expected. Something that seemed to take the whole situation to a much higher level, if that was even possible.

"I know those bastards killed my mother, too, because she knew too much, and insisted that the police do something to help me."

I had the statement that Tingsley gave to the police about his relationship with my uncle in a folder in front of me. It was innocuous, and not at all helpful to the police or us in its present form.

"Martin, the first thing I would like you to do is read this paper over. This is a copy of the statement that you supposedly gave to the Lakewood Police Department when they interviewed you right after the murder. You signed it at the bottom," I said, pointing to an area of the form that contained only the top half of his signature. The bottom portion, I suspected, was cut off by the Xerox machine.

Martin took the form, and another cigarette from the pack on my desk, lighting it with his own lighter that fell from his shirt pocket when he lifted it to his neck. He placed the paper so his wife could read it as well.

"Yes, this is my statement, and that's my signature, or at least the top part. But where are the other pages?" he asked.

"That's all we were given, Mr. Tingsley."

❖ ❖ ❖

From start to finish, our meeting with Martin and his wife lasted nearly three hours. It was obvious that we were not given the entire file from the Lakewood PD, but we already knew that. We just didn't know what we were missing, but we were beginning to find out, and more.

Martin explained that he got caught with marijuana when he was in junior high. After that, certain school officials recruited him for sex parties in exchange for that and other drugs, including LSD. As he got deeper into the activities, becoming one of the regulars at these parties, the more drugs they would give him, and the worse he was treated. He described being raped by men and older boys. There were other boys from his school there, as well as some young girls. Except for one other young boy, he knew only their first names.

The older men would take turns performing various sex acts on Martin, and make Martin reciprocate. He said there were times when he was tied up to other boys and blindfolded while he was being raped by men and various objects. He said that the longer scar was from a curling iron that was heated and used to rape him. It got too hot, he said, and he screamed. An older man removed the curling iron from inside of him, replacing it with his own manhood. The burn was caused as the older man purposely turned the iron higher and placed it against his buttons while he was being raped.

Martin was frequently burned at different times, at different parties, by men with cigarettes and cigars. The men would bet money on how long it would take for each boy to scream out in pain, pleading for the hot cherry tip to be removed. He described how the men would take their turns, switching between the boys and the girls. Gina and I both wrote five pages of notes, each page more sickening and troubling than the last.

During our meeting, I asked Martin if I could take photographs of his injuries, assuring him that all photos and evidence would be kept strictly confidential. He agreed. Mary and Gina departed to the outer office while Martin disrobed and I spent forty-five minutes carefully taking photographs of each of the scars on every part of his anatomy. I recorded the photographs on a sheet marked "Photographic Evidence," and placed the rolls of film and the sheet into a manila envelope, locking it in my file cabinet. Afterward, I summoned Gina and Mary back into my office.

I was almost afraid to ask, but I had to.

"Martin, how does my uncle fit into all of this?"

He sighed and grabbed another cigarette from the now empty pack. Mary was holding her husband's hand, and I saw her gently squeeze it as he began to answer this question.

Martin's speech started to become erratic. "I saw him arrive at one of the parties. It was a party at a city councilman's house. Jerry was my guidance counselor at school. He was the counselor the school assigned to me until I dropped out. It was odd when I saw him. I saw him before he saw me. I watched him, and I don't think he knew what was going on, what type of party it was. As soon as he saw me there, he turned away and left in a hurry. I think the whole scene surprised him, maybe even scared him."

"Can you tell me when this was?" I asked.

"It was later, in the summer of 1981. I remember it like it was yesterday," he said. I wanted to talk to him about it, but he was on sabbatical. He was supposed to be in Florida with his friend Walter Houghton, but either he never left, or else he came back. I don't know."

"How do you know Walter Houghton?" I asked.

"He was one of the guys taking pictures at some of the parties I was at. There were always guys taking pictures of us, and even video. They would take turns."

"Do you know what happened to the photographs, or the video?" I asked.

"I never saw a picture or video. They went somewhere, but I never saw them."

I felt Martin was holding out on me, but couldn't prove it.

"Damn it, Martin, do you know who killed my uncle?"

"No, Marc, I don't."

"Do you have any idea who might have killed Jerry, if you had to guess?" asked Gina.

"No. Mary and my mother got me straight shortly before his murder. My mother went to the police, and then suddenly, one night, she was dead. They said she died from the injuries in a car accident. But I don't believe them. My mother never drove at night because she had night blindness. They found her inside of the car at the bottom of the bluffs by the lake. They said she missed the turn and ended up down there. I know she would not have been driving. I know it! I want you to look into her murder, too. She was killed because of what she knew, Marc. You gotta believe me!" Martin insisted.

Guided by his wife, Martin provided the names of several men who were regulars at these sex parties. The names were those of some of the richest and most powerful men in and around

Lakewood. He also provided some first names of other boys, and the first and last names of the boys he believed were other victims. To do that, he said that he matched their faces with school yearbook photos from various schools in the area. His mother took him to the library where they spent days looking through the yearbooks. She helped him identify the various people at the parties from the yearbooks and microfiche of the society sections of the newspapers. He said that his mother had a large manila envelope where she kept all of her research. The envelope was never found after her death. Martin suspected that she had her research with her at the time of the accident.

"There is one more thing, Marc," said Martin, "but I don't expect you to believe me. It's okay if you don't." Mary shot him a glance, but gently nodded affirmatively as if to approve of his next revelation.

"What is it?" I asked, finding it hard to fathom any more surprises.

"These guys, these people, have killed. They have ceremonies and are involved in some kind of witchcraft. Satan worship. They have bones, I've seen skulls, they even drink blood," he stammered. They have ceremonies, sacrifices, they wear black hooded robes. I don't expect you to believe me, but I can show you one place where I was taken.

"I thought they were going to kill me, but they wanted me to see what they were doing, and that I could be next. It was way out in a wooded area about ten miles out of town." His voice trailed off.

I bristled at the idea, now thinking that Martin had succumbed to some sort of fanciful delusion as a result of his own experiences. I looked at Mary for any sign of concurrence. She dropped her head and began to weep. "It's true, Marc. Martin took me there after I insisted. We can show you, but I doubt there's any evidence they left to be found. Martin told me who the victim was on that night. He was reported missing. It all fits," she uttered haltingly.

Mary reached inside her purse and handed me a gold plated cross with an over-sized circle on top of it where the chain attached. I looked at it and handed it to Gina, who immediately said "That's an Ankh. Where did you get it, Martin?"

"I stole it from the table at one of the parties I was at. It belonged to one of the men who did this to me. No one knows I have it."

Gina and I looked at each other in silence. "That's the same figure seen etched on the photo album described by Cooper," Gina said after seeing the item.

"I just wanted you to have it in case anything happens to me," said Tingsley.

"That's it? There's no more to this, Martin?" I pressed, moving my view from Mary to Martin, searching for some telltale sign that he was still holding back.

"That's it for now," he replied, becoming jittery and obviously uncomfortable. Saying nothing, his wife reached over and placed her hand on his.

"Okay, thanks. We'll make sure we take a closer look at this during our investigation."

As we finished our meeting, we promised Martin and his wife that we would keep everything confidential until we could determine the best way to help him. Gina hugged Mary and then hugged Martin. I shook his hand, and put my hand on Mary's shoulder as they walked out of the office.

"Be careful," Gina cautioned them both.

Martin stopped in the doorway and turned toward us. "They can't do anything more to me than they've already done. I guess they could kill me, but so what. They already did that a hundred times. It's you two who need to be careful. You guys could end up like my mother."

A chill went up my spine, and I could tell that Gina was equally disturbed by his words of caution.

❖ ❖ ❖

Gina stayed at the office for another hour and a new pot of coffee as we compared notes. We discussed the information provided to us by Martin and his wife, concluding that the timing for our Florida trip couldn't be better.

"Marc, what's up with that satanic symbol? You've had more time to research that aspect of this than I have," Gina said.

"Yeah, I did, but that doesn't make me too much more informed in that area. I need more time. I'll talk to a few people," I said.

"Keep me updated, and I'll do more research too," she said,

concurring with me that this whole case just turned in a very dark and bizarre direction.

We both sat in stunned silence for a few minutes, hearing every creak of the building that penetrated our self-imposed silence.

At 9:45 p.m., Gina apologized for having to leave, but she had to get back home to her daughter. Earlier, I told her I wanted to stay at the office for a little while longer to update the board. Considering the new information, that seemed like a task that could be better done in daylight.

I asked Gina to call me at the office as soon as she arrived home, and she promised she would. I walked her to her car, looking for any vehicles that seemed out of place. I watched as she left the parking lot. She did not appear to be followed.

Thirty minutes later, Gina called and confirmed that she arrived home safe and without accompaniment. After wishing her a good night, I turned my attention back to my notes, and began to conduct background investigations on every name Martin gave to us.

I studied the note, replete with a few names, that Martin provided almost as an afterthought, and considered the implications if determined to be authentic. A shudder went up my spine.

At 11:30 p.m., I sat back in my chair and put my feet up on my desk after turning on the radio to a low volume for some company.

My thoughts drifted to Deana. I wondered if she was sleeping. I longed to see her, to be treated to her beauty, and for the warmth she always radiated.

It was the thought of her that was keeping me balanced between the ugly and profane and the resplendent. While entertaining these thoughts, I drifted into sleep.

CHAPTER 8

Wednesday, May 6, 1987

Annie opened my office door at 6:45 a.m., causing me to wake up with a start. I jumped from my chair and reached for my gun and looked at her. She was stopped dead in her tracks looking at me. We were both surprised to see each other. It seemed like forever as I desperately tried to make sense of where I was and what I was doing. It felt like someone spilled a giant puzzle from a box onto a table top, and I was trying to put the pieces together. I was in that odd state between being awake and asleep.

"Whoa!" she exclaimed. "It's just me, Annie."

My mouth was dry and I was shaky. It took several seconds for me to think back to the last thing I remembered, which was leaning back in my office chair late last night.

"What time did you get in this morning, Marc?"

I mumbled something to her that suggested that I've been here for a while. "What time is it?" I asked.

It's early. It's before seven, and I wanted to make up my time because I left early yesterday.

"Great, Annie. Thanks. Did you make any coffee?"

"Hey, I just got here! I'll put some on now."

"Thanks." She walked to my desk and placed two file folders on my desk containing the hard-copy reports she typed yesterday. "These are for your review and signature," she said. "Why don't you get some sleep, Marc, you're looking pretty rough around the edges."

I sat back down in my chair, still trying to get a grip on the moment. I lit a cigarette and rubbed my temples, as if that would massage me from my stupor. It seemed like it was only seconds later that Annie brought me a cup of coffee and placed it on my desk.

"Wow, thanks Annie." I immediately grabbed the cup of this wondrous dark nectar and lifted it to my lips, not quite hitting my mouth squarely. Coffee dribbled onto my tie and shirt, causing me to grumble a few choice words.

"I draw the line at furnishing bibs and sippy straws," Annie chuckled as she witnessed my uncoordinated efforts to engage in this routine adult activity.

"Funny," I said. "I'm going home for a little bit to change. I'll be back in a few."

Before leaving, I finished my coffee without further dribbles or spills. Despite the sleep I got at my desk, I was still dog tired.

I left the office a few minutes later, headed back to my apartment to shower and change clothes. I took my time at my apartment, drank a pot of coffee, paid some bills, and even gathered some clothes for the cleaners. Clean, freshly shaved and looking better, I returned to the office, arriving back just after 10:00 a.m. Gina had been there for the last hour and Paul had arrived ten minutes before me. Both were in Paul's office where Gina briefed him on the events of the previous evening.

After I had settled in my office, Gina and Paul walked in and sat down. Paul urged me and Gina to write an itinerary of our Florida trip scheduled for next week, including the names of the individuals we planned to interview. He asked for the list no later than tomorrow, but Gina objected, saying that we might develop more leads living in Florida through our continued investigation here. Paul agreed and gave us until Sunday night to provide him with this information.

Gina stayed in my office after Paul left, saying that we had to go over case notes on the various assignments we recently received from paying clients. Instead, we decided upon a course of action pertaining to the information Martin Tingsley provided.

We divided up the names Tingsley had given us, each taking half for the purpose of performing background checks. We both would investigate the death of Martin Tingsley's mother, Bethany Marie Tingsley, by getting a copy of the accident report and related police reports. We also decided to perform a comprehensive background investigation on both Martin and Mary Tingsley to see what kind of skeletons were taking up space in their closets as well.

Before leaving the office, I removed the envelope containing the rolls of film of the photos I had taken of Martin Tingsley's scars from my file cabinet, and put them in my suit jacket pocket.

Gina accompanied me in my car as I drove downtown. On our way down, we stopped at the photo shop where we have an account to drop off the undeveloped film, asking for double prints. We told the shop owner that we would be by sometime later to pick up the photographs.

Upon reaching downtown, I parked near the police department, which was situated midway between the county courthouse and the main public library.

In that area we would spend the remainder of the day scanning through microfilm of old newspapers for reports of the car accident, securing copies of police and accident reports, and looking up criminal and civil histories of each name on our lists.

Although we skipped lunch, our research took us well into the early evening at the public library, which we reserved as our last destination. By 6:00 p.m., we had collected nearly 80 pages of photocopies between us from all locations, in addition to two parking tickets for failing to feed the parking meter.

It was a good day of investigative work and research. Now, we had the daunting task to connect the dots on the information we obtained.

I dropped Gina off at the office while I went back to my apartment. Gina gave me her copies of the documents she obtained so I could sort through them along with mine. As it was now standard operating procedure, Gina called me as soon as she got home to let me know she was alright.

I ordered a pizza from the corner restaurant which arrived in record time. I spent the next few hours eating pizza with my notes spread across the couch and living room floor. Keeping me company on my television were reruns of *Magnum P.I.* followed by *The Equalizer*, interesting choices for entertainment, yet far from the dark reality of what was spread out in front of me.

CHAPTER 9

Thursday, May 7, 1987

I woke up on my couch with the lights and television still on. The bright morning sun created a glare from my east-facing living room window. It was 6:20 a.m. when I swung my feet to the floor and looked down at the mosaic of papers and notes that covered the stained, light blue carpet. I stepped over the half empty pizza box and walked into the kitchen, where I fired up the coffee pot and stood guard as the dark liquid filled the glass pot. The aroma of fresh coffee replaced the stale air of greasy cardboard left over from last night's supper. I filled a mug full of steaming coffee and returned to the living room, where I lit up a Marlboro and scanned the papers in front of me.

After spending nearly a half-hour mentally rehashing Martin Tingsley's accounts of torture and abuse and trying to determine how they fit in to the murder of my uncle, I retreated to the bathroom and spent fifteen minutes under a steady stream of hot water. My thoughts turned from the ugliness of what was slowly consuming my life to the beauty of the woman who I desired most. My mood was elevated by knowing that I would be seeing her in just a matter of hours.

As the situation was still tenuous at best, I wanted to make this lunch date something special. I had to. I had to wash away the dirty, oily darkness in which I felt immersed.

I began thinking of ways I could convey to Deana how much I cared, and how badly I wanted to have a future with her without scaring her away. My heart hurt for her, knowing that her trust and faith had been broken before, which caused her defenses to be on full alert. Perhaps there was something special I could say or do.

Now fully dressed and ready for the day, it was just after 7:00 a.m. I returned to the living room where the television screen featured a self-assured Bryant Gumbel talking about trouble in Lebanon on *The Today Show*. Not wanting the geopolitical update, I switched off the television and turned my full attention back to the array of papers that now seemed to litter the floor without reason. The more I looked, the less I saw. The more I tried to make the pieces fit, the more difficult it became. Nothing seemed to make any sense. I began to think that answers, or at least some of them, might be found in Florida. Or maybe not found at all.

Instead of going to the office this morning, I called Annie to have her tell Paul that I'd be performing field investigations until late afternoon. She accepted the news with a chuckle as she was fully aware of my lunch plans. "Good luck, Marc. Let me know how everything goes," she said. I could detect the smile on her face.

An hour before I was scheduled to pick up Deana, I stopped by a florist and bought her a small bouquet of mixed flowers neatly arranged in a vase. I ran into the neighboring drug store and bought a greeting card that promised her my everlasting friendship and hope for the future, taking a minute to write a few sentences that let her know how often I thought about her, and how much I thought of her. I was hoping to strike the correct balance between a man who genuinely cares and that of a stalker.

She was just walking out into the midday sun as I pulled up to the doors of the business offices. She was wearing a bright white short-sleeve dress with small red dots and a red belt that fit her slender form. She smiled when she saw me. I got out and opened the car door for her, closing it securely after she was safely inside. I pulled away from the front doors and proceeded into traffic, not exactly sure of where we were headed.

"Where would you like to go for lunch?" I asked.

"Anywhere is fine."

"How about Mama Rosa's?"

"That sounds great. I'm hungry and I hear their food is very good. Oh, and I've got an extra half-hour for lunch."

At that moment, I felt like the luckiest man in the world. I am able to spend an extra half-hour with the most beautiful woman in Lakewood! I could feel the school boy coming out in me, but I was careful not to show it.

We were immediately seated at a table at the far end of the restaurant where the lights were low and patrons were few. Instrumental music played softly in the background. A single lit candle inside of an old Italian wine bottle sat on the table in front of us. I noticed hours and hours of wax drippings in multiple colors caked on all sides of the bottle. The ambient light seemed to cast a glow around her. Her unblemished skin looked like fine porcelain, and her wavy brown hair rested across her delicate shoulders.

Our meals arrived quickly, and we finished at the same time. We both skipped desert, choosing instead to spend the remaining time we had together taking a nice drive along the lake shore. There was not a cloud in the sky on this beautiful spring day.

As I drove, I could not help but notice how the sun highlighted her sparkling eyes and her delicate features. Spotting the entrance to a boat dock, I pulled in and parked near the water's edge.

"Deana, I have something for you. I thought this might brighten up your day." I reached behind her seat and handed her the flower arrangement and the card. I had planned, and even rehearsed a follow-up statement, but it never made it from my mouth. I froze like a teenager.

"They're beautiful, I love them! I'll keep them on my desk, and every time I look at them I'll think of you," she said. She leaned over and gave me a warm hug and a peck on my cheek. The light, sweet scent of her perfume was delicately transferred to my suit coat.

She placed her hand on my arm and told me that she would open the card later, when she was alone. She asked about my schedule for my upcoming trip to Florida, and I gave her as many details as I could.

"May I call you from there?" I asked. "I might need to hear a friendly voice."

"Yes! Please do," she responded enthusiastically. "Please be careful driving and whatever you'll be doing there," she added.

"I will."

We looked out across the water at two sailboats that appeared to be on their first outing this spring. "The water is beautiful," she said. "It's so peaceful here. I could stay here all day."

"Well, I've got the time."

"It's really tempting, but I've got to be getting back. I'm sorry."

"I am too, but hopefully, we can do this again?"

"Of course. I'll look forward to it. As soon as you get back, it's a date," she said, seeming to warm up to the idea of spending more time together.

I waited and watched her walk back into the office building. I was already missing her.

❖ ❖ ❖

On my way to my office, I stopped at the photo shop to pick up the packages of pictures of Martin Tingsley's scars from the rolls of film I dropped off the previous day. After quickly scanning them to make sure they turned out, I put them and the negatives in my briefcase with the ever-growing file folder.

I got to the office just after 2:00 p.m. Annie was busy typing and Gina was sitting at her desk in my office.

"Hey, there you are, Romeo! Tell me all about it," urged Gina.

I felt like Gina and I had become sole cop-like partners in the murder investigation. As partners often do, especially in police work and the PI business, they share some of their personal life with each other.

So, I shared a few details, telling her that we went to Mama Rosa's and had a wonderful lunch. I also told her that I gave her a small bouquet of flowers for her office.

"Nice touch, Romeo!"

"Gina, you gotta stop calling me that!" I insisted. "You're giving Romeo a bad name."

Gina smiled, but her smile slowly faded as I removed the pictures from my briefcase and placed them on her desk. She opened the envelope, removed one set of photos and handed me the duplicate along with the negatives. I immediately placed the photos and the negatives in a plastic evidence envelope and locked the package in my file cabinet.

I turned to Gina and told her that I had forgotten to stop at the convenience store on my way to the office. "I need cigarettes, do you want anything," I asked.

"I need some too, and I have something to tell you, so I'll ride with you, okay?

"Sure, let's go."

As I drove to the store, Gina told me that while I was having lunch, she was in the office completing some paperwork. Paul was out meeting with a prospective security client, and she was alone in the office.

"No sooner did Annie leave, the phone rang. I picked it up and it was some guy on the other end. He sounded older, maybe in his fifties, I don't know. He asked for you and I told him you were out," she said.

"Something tells me that he wasn't calling to wish me luck on the murder investigation," I said.

"Good call Dick Tracy. When I asked if I could take a message, he said 'Yeah, tell him that if he goes to Florida, there's a very good chance he'll be coming back in a pine box.' Before I could say anything else, he hung up."

"Was there anything to indicate where he was calling from? Any background noise you could identify?"

"Nothing, Marc. That was it."

"What's your gut telling you, Gina? Do you think it's a crank, just someone who read about our plans in the paper and is just screwing with me?"

"I don't think so. The guy sounded very calm and casual. He sounded really sure of himself."

"Having second thoughts about going with me?"

"I wouldn't miss it for anything. This will be even better than Disneyland," Gina said. "I left a note for Paul to mark the time on the audio tape. You can listen to it when he gets back."

Upon returning to the office Gina handed me her notes detailing the findings from the background investigation she performed for Aetna. I carefully reviewed her findings.

"The guy is clean," she said. "I checked under every rock I could think of. I even managed to get his college transcripts and by a stroke of luck, or more precisely, through a friend who owed me a huge favor, I even got his financials from his bank."

"Wow, I'm impressed!"

"Me too. Too bad he's married and not about 20 years younger. He's averaging in the mid-six figure range on deposit for the last two years. I'd love to have that kind of financial stability."

Paul never came back to the office. Gina and I completed our day by putting the final touches on the background investigation and other notes from various client investigations. I took the file notes from my uncle's murder investigation and placed them in my briefcase and made it back to my apartment by six.

Gina called me just before 7:00 p.m. to let me know she made it home alright. It was good to enjoy a quiet evening. Instead of further obsessing over the details of the case, I cracked open a beer and parked myself on my couch, lost in the thoughts of my lunch with Deana.

CHAPTER 10

Friday, May 8, 1987

Friday began with bright sun just starting to break through the morning mist at 6:15 a.m. I was at my desk by 7:30, pouring over my file notes and rearranging index cards on my cork boards. About 45 minutes into my efforts, I realized that we had not followed up on the telephone lead from a man who only identified himself as Roland, and who had given his telephone number as the Ruby Slipper Lounge. I wrote the information we had on a new index card in red magic marker, pinning it to the bottom right of the board. I also noted on the card to contact after 6:00 p.m., which I believed would be the most likely time to reach him at that location.

An hour-and-a-half, a pot of coffee and a half a pack of cigarettes later, Annie arrived at the office. She seemed to be making a lot of noise on purpose, perhaps recalling our early morning encounter the day before yesterday. I walked into the outer office to wish her a good morning.

"Are you ready for your trip next week?"

"Getting there," I replied.

A few minutes later, Gina walked in to my office, grabbing a cup of coffee along the way. She walked over to the boards on the wall and noticed the index card with the information about Roland and the Ruby Slipper Lounge. "I forgot about him," she said, pointing at the card. "We should do something with this today," she said.

"I'm game. We're going to have to do it later in the afternoon, though."

"That's fine, because I've got to handle a few things with my daughter and her school before we leave Monday."

I spent the day working on various insurance related assignments in the field, while Gina completed some paperwork and left the office early to handle her personal issues. We planned to meet back at the office at 5:00 p.m.

When I got back to the office at 4:45, I saw a note on my desk that was written by Annie. It was a telephone message from Gina, who said that she was involved in a family matter that needed her attention for the majority of the day and evening. She offered to come in tomorrow to work the Ruby Slipper Lounge angle if I wanted. I was to call her when I got the message.

I picked up the phone and called her. As it sounded like she had a lot going on with her daughter, and considering the timing of our upcoming trip, I suggested that we put off the Ruby Slipper Lounge inquiry until sometime after our return from Florida. Sounding relieved, she agreed.

Given her personal issues and the fact that we had not briefed Paul on the latest case developments, we planned to meet back in the office at 8:00 a.m. Monday. We also planned to leave late Monday afternoon for our road trip to Miami, giving us both time on Monday to handle anything that might arise over the weekend and meet with Paul to discuss our travel plans.

I spent the next few hours reviewing and making copies of the critical notes of our investigation that I planned to take with us to Florida. When I felt certain all of my notes were fully up-to-date and in chronological order, I placed the copies into my briefcase and left the office.

When I arrived at my apartment, I sat in the quiet, contemplating the events of the last few weeks. I remained troubled by many aspects of this case, and spent time reflecting on its more sinister parts. My thoughts turned to the final minutes of my uncle's life that played in my head like the ending scene of the movie *Looking For Mr. Goodbar*, which was no longer just a movie to me. It was becoming a haunting template that I constantly replayed in my mind. I had turned it into my own personal cinematic nightmare by immersing myself into the murder case I so readily accepted. Cue the strobe lights.

Despite the swamp of alligators which we apparently wandered into and were wading about, I wondered who would want us followed and why, and who would want to threaten me about our upcoming trip. I felt that I was missing something important, yet whatever it was eluded me.

I was physically tired and mentally frustrated as I obsessed over the known and unknown, the mundane and the fantastic. I felt emotionally beaten. I felt robbed of my childhood memories, for at least I should have those. Yet, those joyful memories have been unceremoniously pushed aside and replaced by newer ones, those stained by blood. I felt robbed of my mother who I missed so much, and now my entire family. I felt alone and lonely. Independent of each other, these feelings are troubling. Together, they can become paralyzing.

The only ray of sunshine amid the darkness that I felt consuming me like a black hole in space was a woman who I suspect is much too good for me.

Despite the inadequacy I feel, I know that we could make a life together. Unfortunately, events of life itself sometimes get in the way.

As the time passed in the stillness of the night, I worked to turn my frustration and self-pity into a plan of action. A new cinematic production with a happy ending, where the good guy wins and gets the girl. I wanted it so badly that I would move mountains if I had to. After all, good things in life rarely come easy.

I turned on the television to cancel out the sense of loneliness. Oh, the oddities in life, I thought, when the final few minutes of *Miami Vice* played out before me on the small screen. The glamour and slick appearances made me laugh as I thought about the palm trees and boats I might myself see next week. I thought about the contrast between hard reality and the illusion before me. Finely dressed and quick-witted cops with fast cars and an even faster boat. Big guns shot with apparent impunity at readily identifiable bad guys without the need for reams of paperwork that follows. Glamorous girls and pristine settings, with a pet alligator thrown in for good measure.

I left the television on as I rested my head on the arm of the couch, choosing sleep over the conflict that exists between fantasy and reality.

CHAPTER 11

Prepping

Some people immerse themselves into their work by their intense desire for success. Often, these people work with such drive that their personal lives become a casualty of their desires. Other people immerse themselves in work to escape their personal lives. The result is often a distinction without a difference. I was feeling that I was a mixture of each.

I spent the weekend working not only because I wanted to seek justice for my uncle and my family, but because I felt like I had nothing else to do. I was in temporary exile from my children. I had no real friends, no place to go. I felt alone.

I spent as much time working as possible as I felt like a person without a home due to my estrangement from my family. Perhaps it was more of a self-imposed exile. Again, it's a distinction without a difference.

On both Saturday and Sunday, I took advantage of the pleasant spring weather to conduct field investigations pertaining to three open insurance related claims. I performed several hours of surveillance on one man who was allegedly injured in an industrial accident and claims to have lost the use of his left arm.

At his relatively young age, the exposure to the employer's insurance company was well over a million dollars, an amount they had to set in reserve unless we determined that the claim was exaggerated or fraudulent. Perhaps it was because of the nice weather or just plain luck that I secured video footage of this man using a sledgehammer to replace the sidewalk in front of his house.

Results like that don't come without a price, even if modern detective shows suggest otherwise. For that critical piece of footage, I spent a total of thirty hours over a span of a nearly two months, most of those hours crammed into the cargo area of a van parked in the sun and the rain, the heat and the cold depending on the weather. I was confined for long periods without having the convenience of modern toilet facilities, instead having to make less comfortable and most assuredly much less classy arrangements depending upon my fluid intake. There were many long hours of boredom and countless muscle cramps that no investigative report will ever reflect, or any television drama will ever show.

By Sunday night, I seemed to be fully prepared not only for my trip with Gina to seek information about my uncle's life and death, but for my absence from the office as well. I completed a to-do list for Paul, detailing the action needed on other open assignments. I wrote up a list of names of the people we intended to interview, and an approximation of our schedule.

I bought a card for Deana, wrote her a rather lengthy note and placed it inside of the card. I put the card inside the envelope, sealed it and wrote her name on the front. Instead of mailing it, I left it next to my coffee maker.

I also wrote short letters to my kids, and one to my father. All were bittersweet. Just in case.

CHAPTER 12

Monday, May 11, 1987

When Monday morning arrived, I was already at my desk for an hour by the time Gina came in. I completed the last of my notes for the cases I worked the last two days and was finishing the list of people we intended to interview in Florida.

Gina took a seat at her desk and began to gather her notes and files in preparation for our late afternoon departure.

"Ready for a road trip?" I asked.

"Boy, am I ever. I need to get away."

"More problems at home?"

"The same problems, just worse," she replied.

"Is your daughter going to be okay?"

"It's not her who I'm worried about," she said somewhat cryptically.

As we were talking, Paul came in and said good morning to us. He retreated into his office and yelled for us to join him when we had a minute. We went in right away.

"Are you two ready?" Paul asked.

"About as ready as we'll ever be," I said as Gina murmured in agreement.

Annie leaned into Paul's office and grabbed my arm, gently spinning me toward her. "Marc, you've got a phone call."

Overhearing Annie, Paul said that I could take it in his office. Annie, however suggested that I take it in mine. I excused myself and took the call in my office.

"Hello?"

"Hi there. Are you all ready for your trip?" I was surprised to hear from Deana so early, although I decided that I was going to call her before she left her office for the day.

"Who is this?" I asked playfully with a sudden and inexplicable sense of self-assuredness.

"You seem to be in a good mood. Is that because you'll be far away from me?" she asked.

"No, I'm already bummed," I said, as I struggled to remember the name of the song with the lyrics that mentions that although we'll be far apart, we'll still be looking at the same moon and stars. "But I'm really happy you called. What makes me so lucky this morning?"

"I've been thinking about you. I just want to see you before you go. I've got something for you, something for you and Gina to take with you," Deana said. "Can you stop down at lunchtime?"

"Can I take you to lunch, too?" I asked.

"Sure. Is 11:30 okay?"

"It's great for me. I'll see you then," I said as I gently replaced the receiver.

I walked back into Paul's office to join Gina and finish our discussion about our travels. "And make sure you guys take the shotgun." Those were the words just coming out of Paul's mouth when I walked back in.

"Wow, what did I miss?" I asked.

"Not much, Marc," Gina said, as she escorted me from Paul's office and back into mine. "Paul wants to wait until we get back from Florida before we bring him completely up to date on our developments in the murder investigation. He's really involved in getting the security part of the business off the ground, and tight on time. His instructions amounted to "'Be careful, check in to the office twice a day and let him know if we end up in jail or trouble.'"

And there it was. The sum total of our big preparatory meeting with Paul. Take the shotgun, be careful and check in.

"Is there anything we need to do, or anybody we should talk to before we leave, Marc?"

"I don't think so. I'll pick up the car we'll be using. It's got more room and has a bit more power than either of ours. Supposedly more dependable, too, but we'll see. I'll pick up the shotgun on my way to get you," I said.

"Don't forget the shells."

"Oh yeah, I won't," I said as my mind wandered off, thinking about the telephone call I received and wondering what it was Deana had for us to take on our trip.

"Hello, are you in there?" Gina snapped her fingers in front of my face. "What's the matter, is love holding your mind hostage? Do I need to start worrying now, or when we're a thousand miles away?"

"Sorry, Gina. I'm going to lunch with Deana. She called unexpectedly. She's got something for us to take to Florida. I'll pick it up then."

"I hope it's an answer sheet for this case," she said wryly. Before she left the office, we made the final arrangements for our trip. Meanwhile, I counted down the time to my lunch date.

CHAPTER 13

Saying Goodbye

I pulled up to the rear doors at Deana's office at 11:25 a.m. in anticipation of seeing Deana walk out. She is always radiant, and today proved to be no different. She was wearing a dark blue dress with a light coat. Her brown hair fell gracefully over her shoulders and seemed to gently bounce as she walked to my car. She was carrying a large paper bag that appeared to be holding some type of container. I walked around and opened the passenger door for her, closing it behind her as she settled in.

"This is a very nice surprise," I said to her. "Where to?"

"I've got lunch inside, so we can just take a drive, if you want," she said.

"I'd love to." I said, setting off to drive around the lake, taking in the sights of the water and boats, and the smell of the spring air as temperatures were moderating.

"I brought something for you and Gina to take on your trip." Deana reached into the bag and lifted up a large container of cookies. "They're pumpkin cookies. I baked them last night. Want to try one now?" she asked.

"I do." She handed me a cookie and took one for herself. I took one bite into my newest favorite cookie, finishing it in two more.

"They're fantastic! Thank you for thinking about me."

"Now don't forget to share with Gina," Deana warned as she placed the container back into the bag.

We drove for 45 minutes, much of it in comfortable, even reassuring silence. I felt a sense of purpose with Deana, and a hope for a future like I've never felt before. She put her hand on mine, and I locked my fingers into hers. It was the first time I've felt this close to her. We both talked about some of our current and past problems. She shared her joy of having a beautiful child. My mind raced as I silently imagined our future together.

Our time together was painfully short, I thought, as I returned her back to work. Removing her hand from mine, she pulled my head close to hers and kissed me on the cheek, and placed her hand on my arm.

"Marc, please be careful. And please, call me when you can." I detected a sense of concern as she delivered those words, stepping from the car before I could open my own door to let her out. She leaned into the open door and smiled as she reminded me to share the cookies. Smiling back, I assured her that I would comply on all counts.

I watched her walk back into the building, longing for her to suddenly change direction, turn around and come back. She disappeared behind the blandness of the brick and mortar. I knew it would be the last time I saw her until I returned.

CHAPTER 14

Road Trip

It was 6:00 p.m. when I picked up Gina for our investigative excursion to Miami, Florida. For the sake of convenience, I picked her up at a rest stop just off the Interstate, which is just two miles from the mobile home she shares with her boyfriend Bob. At 30 years old, Gina developed into a great investigator and had more courage than most men I knew. She could hold her own in the worst of situations. I was grateful to Paul that he selected her over other investigators as my back-up for our road trip to Miami, Florida.

Gina was in a volatile relationship with Bob, an outwardly friendly guy who likes to drink more than work. Even at her relatively young age, Gina had a 13 year-old daughter who looked and acted more like a young adult than anyone of her age. Although Gina was a bit hesitant to leave her daughter behind for a few days, she knew that her parents would be keeping a close eye on her.

As soon as I pulled into the parking space next to Bob's pick-up, Gina shot out of the passenger side of their vehicle, duffel bag in hand, more ready to leave than I expected. I walked around to the trunk of the green, 1980 Chevrolet Caprice four-door we had borrowed for this excursion.

The odometer had stopped working at 122,512 miles, and the gas gauge was not to be trusted, I was told. My bag and a pump action .12 gauge Mossberg shotgun were already in the trunk. Gina looked at the shotgun and said "Glad you remembered," as she tossed her bag next to mine. "You brought the shells, right?" Gina's question made me realize that we had the equivalent of a metal baseball bat, as I left the shells at the office in my haste to leave.

"Just as I thought," Gina said, and tossed a box of shells onto the back seat. "You owe me five bucks," she said. Seconds later, we were headed south on the Interstate, mentally preparing ourselves for the uncertainty that awaited our arrival.

We figured that by leaving at six we would arrive in Miami sometime around five Tuesday afternoon, leaving about two hours for bathroom stops and the unexpected. That would give us plenty of time to check out the area, find a motel, get a good night's sleep, and then set up surveillance of Houghton's estate the following morning, or so we thought. Unsure of what we might find, we wanted to see the car he was driving, and perhaps see if he was living with anyone we did not know about. We wanted to check the area late at night and in the pre-dawn hours when most people are asleep or barely awake.

I suggested that we take turns driving, switching with every gas fill-up. That would give us both enough time to sleep for a couple of hours while the other drove. It sounded good in theory, at least.

Before picking up Gina, I stopped at the local mini-mart to grab some last-minute essentials that included a dozen Twinkies, a couple of bags of pretzels, some soft drinks and, of course, two extra-large cups of coffee. We both finished our coffee before we hit the county line.

We took inventory of our travel money and fallback credit cards. Between us, we had $345.00 in cash and some change, and a few well-used credit cards, most approaching their limit. It was less than reassuring. We had the burgeoning investigative file, a handful of worn road maps and a road atlas, and a general idea of the route we would take to get to Miami. I also brought the homemade baked delicacy given to me by Deana earlier in the day.

Reaching over the seat into the back of the car, I produced a paper bag with the container of cookies inside and placed the bag next to Gina. "Okay, I've got a confession to make. I've been holding out on you, but I promised Deana I'd share. The Twinkies are just our fall back. You've got to taste one of these homemade pumpkin cookies from Deana. They will tickle your taste buds and forever change the way you look at all baked goods," I promised. Gina removed the container from the bag, took a cookie and handed me one.

"Hey Romeo, there's a note in here. Want me to read it to you while you're driving?"

"No, that's fine, just give it to me."

"Nah, I think I'll open it and read it to you," she said playfully.

"Just hand me the note, slowly place the bag on the seat, and move slowly away from the bag. And keep your hands where I can see them," I joked.

❖ ❖ ❖

At some point in the darkest point of the night, somewhere near Wytheville, Virginia, we found ourselves off the interstate we were supposed to follow. Amid the rain, darkness and fog rolling down from the mountains, we got so twisted around that we ended up traveling north instead of south.

At one point we found ourselves on the path that would take us down the western part of the U.S. toward Tampa instead of the eastern coast of Florida. That cost us dearly in both time and patience.

As night began to turn into day and clear skies turned into the gray mist of rain, we made gas stops in Fayetteville, North Carolina and Walterboro, South Carolina. Finally, nearly 24 hours after leaving Lakewood, we were stuck in the rush hour traffic of Jacksonville, Florida.

Tired and drained from the drive and several hours behind schedule, we stopped at a rest stop just off the interstate. I wanted to use a pay phone so I could make the call I had been looking forward to making for the last 24 hours. It was 4:40 pm. In just 20 minutes, Deana would be leaving her desk and I wanted so badly to hear her voice and talk with her.

Dipping into a pocketful of dimes and quarters, I made the call, only to learn that she left early for the day. Damn, I thought, nothing is going as planned.

We continued south on I-95 through Melbourne and Palm Bay, Florida, yet our destination seemed to be getting farther away, rather than closer. Due to the weather, traffic tie-up and after countless times of being re-routed due to construction, we arrived in Miami shortly before 2:00 Wednesday morning, some 32 hours for a trip that should have taken us no more than 24 hours.

We were both tired, agitated and none too fresh by the time we pulled up to the Everglades Inn Motor Lodge, a two-story drive-to-your-room type of motel.

We both went inside to talk to the night clerk, asking for a room with two beds or some type of efficiency that would provide us some semblance of personal privacy.

The night clerk was a thin, heavily tattooed middle-aged man who made no attempt to hide the fact that we were taking him away from whatever late night television programming he was watching on a small, back-and-white set.

The television was positioned on the side of the customer counter in such a way that he did not need to move to take care of any customer that might walk in. Before I could ask if any rooms were available, and without taking his eyes away from the TV, he blurted out "one room left, a single, two beds, with air conditioning and cable television, thirty bucks up front."

As he was talking, Gina drew my attention to a large, ugly brown bug that appeared quite comfortable on the wall behind him. I had no idea what kind of bug it was. A roach, perhaps, but it was enough for me to tell him that we would "check back a little later."

"Suit yourself, but the room might not be vacant when you do," the clerk warned.

"Thanks, but we'll take our chances," I said as the office door shut behind us with a bang. As we walked back to the car, we both burst out laughing and made references to the Alfred Hitchcock movie *Psycho*.

After driving for another 45 minutes, stopping at motels that were either filled or we could not afford, we decided to take the room at the Everglades Inn. We walked in to the motel, noting that the clerk was still glued to the television.

"Okay, we'll take it," I told the clerk. That caused him to look up at us, at which time we could see his facial features and expression.

He made no effort to conceal his actions as he looked Gina up and down, looked me in the eyes, and spit a wad of chewing tobacco into the nearby trashcan.

"That will be fifty bucks, and checkout is at noon," he said.

"Wait, you told us thirty dollars less than an hour ago," I protested.

"Yeah, well, those were yesterday's rates. Do you want it or not?"

Tired, unimpressed and quite irritated by his demeanor, including the mental undressing he did of Gina, I reached over the counter and grabbed the clerk by his shirt with both hands, lifting him off his feet and pulling him onto the counter.

"I got thirty bucks and a really bad attitude right now. We'll take the thirty-dollar room," I said, bringing his face close enough to mine where I could smell his acrid breath of chewing tobacco and rotted teeth.

Responding to the situation, Gina quickly pulled out her badge, holding it far enough away that he could not distinguish us from police or any other agency that could cause him potential problems. Seeing the badge, the clerk immediately became docile, put his hands up toward his head, suggesting personal familiarity of the drill, and indicated his compliance. At that point, I let him go and watched as he regained his footing with the floor.

Without saying anything, he pulled a small index card from the counter and instructed me to write my name and address on the card. He placed one metal key on the counter in place of the three ten dollar bills I placed there after I let him go.

Without looking at the bogus information I wrote on the card, he filed it in a shoe box under the television set.

"Room 213, top of the outside steps, on the left."

Gina walked out the door first, and we both got back in the car as we moved it another 20 feet to a parking space at the bottom of the steps. We could see the clerk watching us as we unloaded our bags from the truck. Gina grabbed the shotgun, making sure he saw it as she carried it up the steps to our room.

Walking up the steps, Gina quietly registered her objections about my behavior.

"Honestly, Marc, I've got to watch you everywhere we go. I can't take you anywhere."

Under my breath, I responded with my best Clint Eastwood impression, "Nag, nag, nag." Of course, I'm no Clint Eastwood or Dirty Harry. After all, a man has got to know his limitations.

We opened the door to a dark, musty, room with a stained orange carpet and two double beds that were covered in orange colored bedspreads. Gina turned the light on in the bathroom and let out a small screech upon seeing a small gecko scurry from the dated coral blue bath tub. With the room door still open, the gecko scurried out of the room and onto the cement steps.

We took turns showering before finally making it to bed. By the time we got settled, it was almost a 3:30 a.m. Gina took the bed by the air conditioner and I took the bed closest to the door.

We thought about asking for a wakeup call, but decided against it. Instead, I set my travel alarm to five o'clock, giving us about 90 minutes of good, solid sleep.

Despite utter fatigue, neither one of us could sleep. The air conditioner was not working and the room was hot and musty. At 4:45 a.m., I showered again, shaved, changed into my suit, walked to the car and drove to the nearest all-night McDonald's for coffee. As I walked into the motel room, Gina was already up and packing her things. We both decided that we would not stay another night in this motel, considering the 'incident' with the night manager.

After packing and reloading the car with our belongings, we drove to the office where Gina ran in and dropped off the room key. It was nearly 5:30 a.m. Both Gina and I were back in the car, headed for the residence of Walter Houghton.

We just pulled out of a parking lot when Gina began to laugh hysterically. Somewhat irritated, I asked Gina what was so funny. Between a series of snorts and giggles, Gina said that I was dressed exactly like "Sonny Crockett" from *Miami Vice*, minus the nice car. I adjusted the rear-view mirror and looked at myself, and began to laugh with her.

On the other hand, she looked like she just left a model shoot. She looked good and smelled even better. Her dark brown hair was impeccable and seemed to glisten in the low lights of the neon signs and street lamps.

We took up our surveillance position at 5:45 a.m., well behind our self-imposed schedule. Upon our arrival, I did a quiet "walk-around" of the property as the sun was making its way above the horizon. As I walked behind the residence, I caught a glimpse of an older man walking barefoot in his boxers letting out a yappy dog from the residence behind Houghton's. Although I was startled by this early riser, I exhibited confidence and gave him a good morning nod, acting like I belonged there. There was only one car parked at Walter Houghton's residence, and nothing I saw from my close inspection or we observed collectively indicated that there was any other permanent cohabitant at this location.

At ten minutes to seven, both Gina and I were bursting at the seams from the coffee we drank. Violating the most basic rule of surveillance, we decided to find the closest fast food restaurant to quickly take care of business. Imagine our surprise when we returned to our surveillance position to find that Walter Houghton had left in our absence. I burst into an expletive-filled diatribe directed to no one in particular.

"Feel better now, Marc?" Gina asked when I was done.

She apologized for not having the physical anatomy to use an empty jar, and I apologized for my fit of anger. We agreed that we needed to clear our heads and salvage the day.

Since we already had the vehicle description and the plate number, we proceeded to the school where Walter works. We verified his presence, his start time and also the time he was expected to leave by making inquiries with a couple of teachers on the premises. We did so in a manner that lessened the possibility that our inquiries would get back to Houghton before we had a chance to talk to him.

While Houghton was still busy teaching, Gina suggested that we seek out additional potential witnesses in this special, distinct section of suburban Miami, yet close to downtown. She opened the file and selected one person in particular, which is the interior designer with whom Walter reportedly has a very close relationship. Unsurprisingly, his name is Percy Bridgeworth.

"How fitting," she said pointing to his name on the witness sheet. At that point, our sleep deprivation got the best of us. We both burst into uncontrollable laughter. Passersby looked at us seated in the car, laughing as tears rolled down our faces, mixing with the light sheen of sweat as a result of the sub-tropical humidity of the morning.

CHAPTER 15

Percy Bridgeworth

We arrived at Miami Interior Design located in an upscale business area of the city and waited for the arrival of Percy Bridgeworth. It was approximately 10 minutes to nine when we saw a short, rotund balding man opening the front door of the storefront with a key. Five minutes later, we watched as Mr. Bridgeworth unrolled a decorative awning over the front window of his store. When he was almost finished, we exited the car and approached Mr. Bridgeworth.

"Hello, Mr. Bridgeworth," I said as Gina and I approached him. We both displayed our badges and introduced ourselves. He was more flamboyant and animated than we could have ever anticipated. He invited us into his store, which was pleasantly air conditioned and of course, exquisitely decorated with a mix of fine furniture and large swatches of fabric.

The interior entrance to the store did not seem to match its surroundings. We noticed a black and white checkerboard floor that served as the entryway, while the rest of the floor was a combination of bamboo planks and carpeting.

Despite the nice displays of upscale home furnishings, the store had a musty aroma. It was like walking into the attic of your grandmother's house without the chests and boxes of stored items. Air fresheners in the scent of tropical flowers were strategically placed around the store, but they only served to mix the musty air with a sweet odor. It was as if the two scents were fighting for dominance over one's olfactory sense in some unseen battle.

As we walked to the middle of the surprisingly large showroom, a small dog sporting two ribbons on the top of its head came prancing out from somewhere in the back.

"Oh, this is 'Mr. Belvedere,' my Norwich Terrier" Bridgeworth said as he reached down and picked him up. He held him close to his chest and talked to him like an infant, walking closer to allow us the privilege to pet his dog and receive a tongue bath should we desire.

"Mr. Belvedere, say hello to our visitors, they traveled all the way from Lakewood to see us," his childlike voice and mannerisms causing waves of nausea to briefly overcome me. I could see that Gina was desperately trying to hold back laughter. You just can't make this stuff up, I thought, and reached out my hand to greet the overly friendly dog.

After being introduced to Mr. Belvedere, Bridgeworth put the dog back to the floor and called out for 'Freddy,' someone who was apparently in the back room of the store. As soon as he called his name, a man far more than half the age of Bridgeworth walked toward us. Freddy, as we were to learn, was Bridgeworth's store helper and also his live-in domestic companion.

Freddy was a tall, muscular young man dressed in tight, stone washed jeans and a snugly fitting muscle shirt that seemed way too short for him or any male for that matter. The shirt revealed a tuft of black hair on his stomach, extending from the top of his jeans to just under his shirt.

The size of his arm muscles suggested that he spends most of his time working out. Mentally, I tried to determine his age, thinking that he could not be too far out of his teenage years, if at all. His blond hair was combed back and smelled of fruit, although I could not discern which type. Fitting nonetheless, I thought.

"Freddy, I'd like you to meet Marc Stiles and his partner, Gina—I'm sorry dear, I forgot your last name."

"It's Russell."

"Russell, well thank you Ms. Russell. Freddy, would you mind getting my visitors here a beverage? What would you two like?"

I learned from experience that if someone offers you a drink at the start of an interview, you take it, as it can be used to extend the contact if necessary. It also seems to break down various other barriers that might otherwise exist in situations such as this.

"Yes, thank you, coffee, just black," I requested, and Gina asked for the same, with cream. With that, Freddy disappeared to the back room.

"Come, sit, the both of you." Bridgeworth pointed to an antique sofa and matching chair. He sat in the chair and Gina and I took the sofa, not expecting the hardness of the fabric covered cushion.

"It's late nineteenth century Victorian, imported from France. If you like it, you can take it with you. I'll give you a nice deal on it, three thousand dollars for the set." Bridgeworth ran his hand across the arm of the chair. "This is my favorite piece, except for Freddy, of course," he chuckled. "I like my furniture vintage, not my toys," he said with an animated smugness that began to become seriously off-putting.

Just then Freddy delivered the three of us drinks that he carried on an ornate silver platter. Our coffee was in china cups and saucers that seemed to match the Victorian theme. Without having to ask, Freddy brought Bridgeworth iced tea in a tall glass with a lemon wedge and a sprig of mint on top of the glass.

"Thank you my dear," he said to Freddy as he placed the platter on the equally ornate coffee table in front of the sofa. He then slapped Freddy lightly on his butt as he reached to pick up his glass from the platter, giggling like a school boy.

Gina quickly looked away. I could not tell whether she was trying to withhold laughter or attempting to hide her disgust. In either case, the display of affection that was more a theme of dominance and ownership did not sit well with either of us.

"So, what can we do for you two?" Bridgeworth asked. He is either using we as a royal pronoun or is including Mr. Belvedere in the conversation, I thought.

I started. "I believe you know why we're here. We want to know everything there is to know about my uncle's friends and activities here in Miami. We want to know about his relationship with Walter Houghton, and anything you could tell us about his life. We are going to find out who killed him, Mr. Bridgeworth," I said, emphasizing the last sentence as I leaned forward, intentionally invading his personal space.

The giddiness he exhibited turned to a sudden, unexpected darkness of expression I had rarely seen before. His look sent a shiver up and down my spine, and also caused me to wonder where Freddy 'six-pack' was at this moment, and if he was watching us from some hidden perch in the rear of the store. In that moment, our eyes locked. I could sense intense hatred, although I was unsure if it was his or mine, or maybe a combination of both.

The sub-tropical air turned cold, yet I felt beads of sweat forming on my forehead and under my shirt.

"You're not going to find the murderer down here, Mr. Stiles." Bridgeworth verbally punched out my name for emphasis, in defiance of my assertion. But then, he sat back in his chair and began to speak not in sentences, but in long paragraphs. Gina was taking notes as he spoke, while I kept my eyes locked on his every move.

"Your uncle was out of control. He was a drunk who was doing any guy he could. He trolled the bars, anyplace where he could find a one-night stand. He broke Walter's heart, you know. They had planned to retire and live together here in Miami, or at least that's what Walter thought. That is, until Walter paid him a surprise visit in Lakewood last fall. Walter flew to Lakewood on his birthday to surprise him, except it was Walter who was surprised. When he got to Jerry's house, he found Jerry in bed with some young stud. I'm surprised you didn't know about this."

"Who said I didn't?" I stated with feigned authority. "So, why don't you tell me what happened next?"

"Nothing happened. Walter said little to Jerry, got on a plane and came home. There was no fight or altercation, just a lot of tears. It tore Walter up real bad. He even tried to have your cousin, the priest, talk to Jerry about his drinking and behavior. He really cared for Jerry. Walter wouldn't hurt a fly, if that's what you're getting at."

"So, who was this young stud," I asked." "And just how young was he?"

"Well, that's the other thing. Let's just say very young. Walter told me he learned that the boy was 16 and still in high school. Worse, Walter told me that Jerry had the boy pose for pictures. Polaroid pictures, including some action shots."

"And how do you know this? I asked.

"After they broke up, Jerry sent Walter a few pictures with a nasty note to make him jealous. Jerry was a very sick man you know. Walter try to help him even after Jerry sent him the note and the pictures. Jerry wouldn't listen and didn't want help. He was on a path of self-destruction. Nobody down here was surprised at the news of his death. We thought he'd drink himself to death, or even die from an overdose, or an accident. Murder, however, was not on our radar. Looking back at his lifestyle, I guess even murder should not have surprised us, though." Bridgeworth's voice trailed off.

"Who was the boy?" I asked.

"I don't know, Mr. Stiles. Walter never said. But he was not the only one. He was not the only young boy that Jerry took under his wing."

"How do you know? I asked.

"Because after that incident, Jerry continued to send pictures of other boys in action to Walter. I guess he was trying to make him jealous, or something. Walter thought it was really sad."

"Okay, Mr. Bridgeworth, I think I get it. Walter is a saint, or at least, your typical, run of the mill 'fudge-packer'. Jerry, however, was a pervert. Jerry liked the teen scene, while guys like you and Walter like 'em young but legal. I understand. Yeah, I get it. Your moral compass stops strictly at the legal age of consent. That's some value system you have, if I may say so myself."

"Marc—" Gina began to intervene, but Bridgeworth interrupted.

"How dare you judge me. Just because you can't handle what I'm telling you does not give you the right to insult me."

Perhaps sensing the tension, Mr. Belvedere quickly strutted over to his master. Bridgeworth pick up the dog and placed him on his lap, holding him close to his chest.

Gina quickly interjected. "Mr. Bridgeworth, all we want to know is who killed Jerry. We're not here to judge. It's been a very long couple of days for us, and I'm sure you can understand that this is very emotional for Marc."

I was a bit miffed that Gina interrupted what promised to be a very self-satisfying, biting verbal assault on this very effeminate man-child. But, she single-handedly saved the interview. Although Bridgeworth kept talking, he now directed his answers to Gina and not me. He made a show of crossing his legs and leaning away from me toward Gina, while stroking Mr. Belvedere like a small girl combing a doll's hair.

"Marvelous," I muttered under my breath, and looked around the store at the various decorative items.

I listened as Bridgeworth opened up to Gina, making mental notes of the key points. Walter and Jerry had been in a relationship since their days in the army together. Over thirty years. Outside of one time early in their relationship, they had been exclusive to each other. For the last 15 years, Jerry was paying Walter every month for one-half of their Florida retirement home, which is the house where Walter presently resides. Twice every school year and all during summer break, Jerry would stay with Walter. During Jerry's visits, Walter, Percy, Freddy and others would always spend time together. Bridgeworth provided a list of their regular haunts in the area, along with the contact information for others in their clique.

"It's all harmless fun and entertainment" Percy insisted.

I suffered in silence during the remainder of the interview, having been rendered a virtual spectator in the interview by my own attitude and actions. I listened while Gina wrote down the names and addresses of numerous others who could likely provide more insight into the life, and perhaps the death of my uncle.

Personally, though, I sat there convinced that Percy Bridgeworth along with cabana boy Freddy was guilty of something. He had to be. The dark look I saw in his eyes transmitted unspoken evil. Pure evil.

As Gina concluded the interview, I was more than ready to leave. I wanted to shower. I needed to get my head together. More than anything, I needed to break into the dark underworld hidden by the bolts of fine fabrics and linens that were staged to give the appearance of normalcy. You can't cover the underlying evil with beautiful and eye-catching fabric any more than you can cover the smell of rot with Airwick, I thought.

I led our departure from Miami Interior Design, saying little as I was the first out the door while Gina exchanged pleasantries with Bridgeworth and Mr. Belvedere. I felt sorry for the dog.

❖ ❖ ❖

"What the hell is wrong with you, Marc? You almost blew our chances to get any information from him." Gina continued to scold me while we walked back to our car, and continued her tirade even as I started the car and drove away. I said nothing because I knew that she was right, but I just didn't want to hear it right now. After she finished, I apologized and steered the car into the parking lot of a convenience store.

"Thank you, Gina." It was all I could say at that moment. My head was spinning, my stomach was in knots, and I could feel the coffee I had slowly inching its way up my throat.

I felt like I had a hangover without the fun of a party or other occasion. I kept both hands on the steering wheel and placed my head on my knuckles. Gina put her hand on my arm to show her unspoken support.

"Let's grab some breakfast," she said, "and we can review the information we have now. Let's get a game plan going. We'll make the most of the time we have down here."

Consenting, we had breakfast at a small diner that appeared to be a hot-spot for the residents of this area set away from greater Miami.

We decided that we would conduct one more interview from our newly expanded list of potential witnesses before setting out to find a motel room that would suit our budget. Looking at the list, a name given by Percy caught my attention. Porter Landers.

Porter Landers is the owner of a club aptly called The Yellow Brick Road located in downtown Miami. As it happened, the club was located just off of Tamiami Trail, just two blocks south and one block east from where we were sitting.

After we each finished our breakfast consisting of omelets, toast and coffee, I paid the cashier and we began our walk toward the club owned by Landers. As we turned off of the main street onto Second Avenue, the architecture of the buildings changed dramatically. The new facades sporting a tropical theme on each of the buildings on the main street were absent on the buildings off of the main road.

The healthy palm trees equally spaced on the main road gave way to dead or dying palm trees and brush, giving the appearance of third-world abandonment. Even the air smelled different. Instead of a coconut oil scent that seemed to be wafting in the air on the main road, perhaps from some automatic air freshener hidden by palm fronds, it smelled of rotten produce and acrid desperation.

It's funny how that works, I thought. There is an area consisting of quaint, made-over buildings with fresh facades on every storefront on the main road that please the eyes of tourists and business people alike. Wander off of the approved path, though, and you enter into a completely different world. A world that tourists are not supposed to see. A world that consists of shades of gray, with dirty sand blowing into the alleys and crevices, and litter strewn on the streets and sidewalks. The deeper into this world we walked, the greater the desperation in sight and smell.

It took us just about five minutes to reach Landers' club, which was a two-story unassuming building with a metal front door painted pink.

An engraved white sign with the words 'The Yellow Brick Road' in script was affixed to the front of the building to the right of the door. In the same type of script but in smaller lettering were the words 'Dorothy's Paradise.'

Only one window was visible in the front of the club, and that opening now consisted of glazed window blocks, preventing anyone from seeing in or out.

A small, makeshift parking lot suitable for about a dozen cars was made from an abandoned lot next to the club. The lot was deserted at this hour, although just a cursory inspection determined that it is well used during normal club operating hours.

As I walked through this lot, I saw several freshly used condoms and wrappers strewn about in the small patches of grass and sand that served as a natural perimeter. A few beer bottles also littered the lot. Some were broken while others looked as if they were accidentally abandoned by drinkers who I envisioned became distracted by their deeds outside of the club.

After my impromptu parking lot safari, I walked back toward the front of the building to meet Gina. She pointed to a small sign we missed earlier that had the club hours. The club opened nightly at 10:00 p.m., closed on Sundays.

How thoughtful, taking the Lord's day off from whatever decadence that might exist inside those brick walls. The sign also noted that every Tuesday was 'Leather Night.' Oh boy, I thought, imagining a group of 'Percys' and 'Freddys' dressed like the guys from the Village People.

Considering that the club was closed and no one seemed to be inside at this hour, we continued with our plan of locating a suitable hotel that we could use as a new base of operation. We found a newly renovated Holiday Inn in close proximity to us.

It had a restaurant and bar attached, and advertised room service. Although it was well before check-in time, the clerk allowed us to have the room early. I forked over the $42.00 and we received two room keys.

We were put into room 112 which was on the first floor with exterior access. It was much cleaner than the last room, and there were no bugs or geckos to greet us upon our entry.

Although it was still early and we had showered earlier that morning, we decided another shower would help us think clearer. We flipped a coin to see who would have access first. Gina won the toss, and excused herself as she made her way into the bathroom. I walked to the bar attached to the hotel and downed two glasses of straight bourbon. Feeling a bit more relaxed, I walked back to the room.

I opened the door and was immediately struck by a pleasant blast of cool air combined with the scent of citrus from Gina's freshly washed hair. She was seated at a table by the window in just shorts and a pullover shirt. Her skin glistened as the rays of the sun entered through the floor to ceiling window by the table.

"Where were you?" she asked me with concern in her voice.

"Just checking some things out," I replied.

"Here, sit down," she said as she made room for me at the table. "Let's go over our notes and revise our game plan." Let's check out Houghton first, then we can talk to Porter Landers.

We still had a few hours before Walter Houghton was scheduled to leave the elementary school where he taught. I showered and changed while Gina gathered our field equipment.

❖ ❖ ❖

We left the hotel in plenty of time to see Houghton come home, so we thought we could possibly interview a few of his neighbors to see what kind of a guy he really is.

During our drive to his residence, we calculated a strategy to use on Walter Houghton that included Gina checking his medicine cabinet and bedroom drawers for anything of relevance she could find. The plan was for me to engage Walter in polite conversation about family issues while Gina excused herself to use the restroom. As they say, even the best made plans…

CHAPTER 16

Walter Houghton

Upon our arrival at Houghton's residence, we were surprised to see Walter tending to his flowers in front of his house. He was home long enough to change from his business attire into very short shorts and a sleeveless tee shirt, revealing a very tanned and muscular body, especially for someone 53 years old. "Well, he's home early," Gina said.

We both got out of the car and I introduced Gina to Walter.

"I was wondering when to expect you," he said.

"How's that?" I said.

"I've been keeping tabs on what you've been doing in Lakewood. Millie sent me the newspaper clippings of the case. An uncomfortable silence followed as Walter kept pruning the tropical flowers without looking in our direction.

"Well, I suppose I would be rude if I didn't invite you in." Walter put his pruning scissors down on the bench on the porch and removed his sandals before stepping into the house.

"Do either of you want something to drink?"

"Sure," replied Gina, "I'll take something cold."

"So will I, Walter. Thanks," I muttered, feeling the coldness he exhibited. Clearly, Walter was very suspicious and put off by our presence in Miami.

Before going into the kitchen, Walter pointed to two Victorian style chairs staged nicely in front of a large bay window in the living room, and motioned for Gina and I to sit down. I looked around at the tastefully appointed living area, noting that some of the furniture might well have been obtained from Percy Bridgeworth. From where I was seated, I could see into the hallway and partially into the kitchen. The house was immaculate. It seemed like all the rooms that I could see were painted bright white, an overkill of white. Even the wall to wall carpet was white. Somehow, I felt that the use of white was an unconscious attempt to hide the darkness that existed in Walter's life.

Shortly after Walter brought us each a glass of iced tea and sat on the sofa across from me, Gina asked to use the bathroom. A little premature I thought, but I'll roll with it. I began my questioning.

"Walter, I'll cut to the chase with you. I know that you and Uncle Jerry had a very, um, 'special' relationship. I just want to know the truth about what happened between you and Jerry. I want to know everything, Walter. I want to know what you know, I want to find the man who killed him."

"You are looking in the wrong place, Marc. You wasted a trip for nothing. In fact, I think it's shameful that you are using the murder of your own uncle for publicity purposes. Damn shameful, Marc. You have a lot of nerve to come down here and talk to me, talk to my friends, and make insinuations that lack any basis in fact."

"Look Walter," I said, "we are down here with the best of intentions and I resent the accusation. What's with the sudden attitude?"

I could see Walter's already tanned face becoming red with anger. I watched as the veins in his forehead and in his neck began to bulge with growing anger. Clearly, I thought it odd that Walter began to bear his teeth without any obvious provocation.

"I'll tell you about my attitude. Ever since the murder, your family has treated me like shit. I've done so much for your family, even for you for that matter, especially when you were younger, but since your father and the rest of the family found out about my relationship with your uncle, I am a pariah. I'm a second class citizen. They've treated me like shit and frankly, I resent that."

"Walter, I think they've treated you pretty well considering…"

"Considering what, Marc? Considering that I'm a faggot? That's what you think isn't it? Hell, after finding out that your uncle was a fag, they couldn't even bother to buy him a grave marker."

"Walter, I did not realize there were any problems between you and my family. I had no idea about the grave marker, but I can promise you I will find out."

I can't explain it, but I actually began to feel sorry for Walter. Obviously, he was dealing with a lot of pain and feelings of rejection. But I was beginning to worry about his escalation, and his building anger toward me. I saw the same look in his eyes that I saw earlier that day from Bridgeworth. While he claimed to be hurt, the look in his eyes projected something entirely different. It was a deep hatred, ensconced in evil that was particularly disconcerting.

"Well you can take a yourselves back to Lakewood and tell your father and your uncle, and your entire family for that matter that they should be ashamed of themselves. Ashamed at the way they treated me, and the way they treated Jerry, even in death.

"And you, Marc, you should be ashamed of yourself for profiting on the death of your uncle. The only reason you're involved in this case is to make a name for yourself. And I think that's disgusting!"

As his response reverberated inside my brain, my sympathy quickly turned to anger. Here I was, face to face with a man I had once respected, berating me as his 'junk' was exposed through the leg opening in his shorts. As I stared at Walter, searching for something to say, the verbal assault against my father and my family began to percolate deep inside the recesses of my mind. I could feel an intense anger building.

"Walter, this is not some PR gig I'm involved in. I could care less about the publicity, and frankly, even less about your hurt feelings. I'm here to do a job, and I'm not leaving until I get some answers."

Suddenly, Walter jumped up and put his finger into my chest, something I do not take kindly. "You get the hell out of here and tell your bastard family to go to hell."

"Walter, get your finger out of my chest and sit down. I want to show you copies of my uncle's bank statements and canceled checks for thousands of dollars that were written to you as recently as the week before his murder. I want to know what these are about, given that you two supposedly ended your relationship." I was doing my best not to let my anger get the best of me.

"That's none of your damn business, Marc, and I'll be damned if I answer you about anything. You have no right to investigate me.

Don't you think that I don't know who you already talked to today? I know everything you are doing. You think you're so smart, but you're not." By now, Walter was visibly shaking.

"Don't turn this around on me, Walter. I know about the pictures of Jerry with young boys, and I presume you saved them. What I'd like to know is if the relationship was over, and Jerry was not welcome back here, why in the world which he continue paying on a house he knew that he could never step foot in again? Could it be that you were blackmailing him, Walter? I think that's a pretty good possibility, don't you?" The knowledge about the pictures and the monthly payments were my 'trump card.' For better or worse, I just showed my hand.

Just then, Gina appeared in the hallway, walking back toward the living room where we were seated. Perhaps it was because my attention was diverted to her that I did not see Walter lunging forward at me. I felt a pain on the left side of my head and face as Walter hit me with his fist while I was still seated. I managed to block a second punch, and plunged my foot into his midsection to push him back into the couch. He landed with a thump, followed by a thud as his head hit the wall behind him.

Gina ran into the room and positioned herself between us. "Stop it! she yelled. Both of you, just stop it."

"Get the hell out of my house, you two, and don't ever come back. Don't even think about talking to anyone else down here. Just get into your car and go back home if you know what's good for you. You have no idea what you've gotten yourselves into."

Had it not been for Gina, I suppose I might have stayed a bit longer. Gina grabbed me by the arm and pulled me to the door. We were followed closely by Walter, who was making certain that we did not tarry. As I opened the car door, I advised Walter that I was not done with him. He responded with an obscene gesture.

"I can't leave you alone anywhere, can I?" Gina stated with a level of agitation in her voice. "Are you all right? It looks like he landed a pretty good one."

"I'm fine. I got in one of my own in too as you saw. So, what did you find out from your little bed and bath expedition?"

"I checked the bathroom and also got into his bedroom. I found nothing of note in either room. It looks like Walter lives alone. One toothbrush. Just his clothes, or it so it seems. I did notice a lock box inside of his bedroom closet. It was locked and I did not see a key anywhere. Maybe if I had more time before you kids started acting up, I might have been able to look more."

"Yeah, I'm sorry about that. I didn't expect that reaction, Gina."

"With you, I never know what to expect."

CHAPTER 17

Porter Landers

We arrived at the stately home of Porter Landers shortly before 3:00 p.m. By our standards, his home was a mansion, complete with a circular driveway and a frontage that included cement statues that towered above a man-made pond. Water trickled from the statues of unclothed men holding what appeared to be vases tilted downward, allowing the stream of water to splash in the pond. Tropical flowers of all colors seemed to be everywhere, and a small area of well-manicured grass separated the pond from the driveway.

As we pulled our vehicle onto the driveway to the front of the house, we noticed a Rolls Royce parked under a carport. Our 'vintage' and well-worn car was decidedly out of place.

As we exited the car, we could see a bit of the back yard. More statues, but this time they towered over a large, in-ground pool. Gina looked at me and commented on the stark differences between where we stood versus the club that we recently left.

We walked to the over-sized set of mahogany front doors and rang the doorbell, which created a sound like Big Ben even from where we stood.

About thirty seconds later, the doors were opened by a young man dressed in a very short, gray and black shiny, satin robe. He seemed to be a near clone of Freddy, sporting a nice tan and a trim, muscular upper body. His blond hair was nicely done, and the top front of his robe was open to reveal two very heavy gold chains around his neck.

"Yes?"

Gina and I produced our badges and identification and requested to speak to Mr. Landers.

"Come in," said this young man, stepping aside to reveal a large foyer appointed with the biggest crystal chandelier I've ever seen. Large pots of plants and flowers created a tropical atmosphere inside this estate, set upon a marble floor that spanned across either side of an ornate staircase that led from the second floor to the foyer. "I'll summon Mr. Landers."

Summon? I thought. Who talks like that, especially considering his age.

"Marc, did you see what he had around his neck?" Gina asked.

"I sure did. The same cross-like talisman that Martin gave us. The same symbol on the photo album. It's called an Ankh, right? I whispered.

"That's it. Same size, too, it seems."

As we waited for Landers to appear, we toured the foyer and peered into the living areas.

"Get a load of this place. I could fit my whole house in here," Gina whispered to me as we stood close to each other. Looking down, I was amused that I was standing on a white and black checkerboard floor, much like the floor in the interior design store.

Suddenly, a well-tanned man who looked to be in his late fifties, with well-trimmed salt-and-pepper hair appeared at the bottom of the staircase. He was cinching the belt on his short robe, one that appeared to match that of the young man who answered the door. He too was wearing gold chains around his neck and diamond rings on both hands.

"Luke tells me that you're the police. What are you, vice?" asked Landers in a rhetorical manner. "I know just about all you people in vice."

"I'm, sure you do," I said, looking him up and down.

I proceeded to introduce us to Landers. After understanding the purpose of our visit, he motioned for us to follow him to the back veranda that overlooked the pool and large, expansive grounds. Being a professional pervert must pay pretty well, I thought.

"Sit, sit" he said, pointing to two cushioned chairs sporting a large floral print that were placed near a large patio table covered by an umbrella. Landers sat in the chair opposite us, and beckoned for the young man who answered the door.

"Luke, I'd like you to meet Gina and Marc. They are private investigators from Lakewood here to talk about the murder of Marc's uncle. You gave me such a start, Luke, when you told me the police were here." Landers made a show of putting his hands over his chest as he spoke to Luke, feigning heart trouble at the suggestion that vice cops were paying him a visit.

"Now won't you be a dear and get our guests some refreshments," Landers instructed Luke. Unlike Bridgeworth's cabana boy, Luke quickly disappeared without taking our requests.

"I've been expecting you. Marc, I'm so sorry to hear about the unpleasantries with Walter Houghton. He can be a bit of a handful, you know. Would you like some ice for your head?"

"Nah, I'm good."

Does this town have a crier? Is there a homosexual hotline? I silently wondered.

"Well, Mr. Landers, you seem to know a lot," said Gina.

"Not just a lot, I know everything," he replied as he flicked his hand, limp-wristed, in Gina's direction.

I moved slightly in my chair in reaction to his reply. Judging by the soft kick to my leg by Gina's foot that was meant as a warning not to turn nasty, she could tell that I was growing tired of the animated, effeminate behavior the men of Miami were exhibiting.

"Well then, you know who killed Marc's uncle," Gina retorted.

"Oh my, no, no, I don't know that, my dear girl. I can tell you who didn't kill him, though. It certainly wasn't Walter, that's for sure. Or anyone from here that he knew. We all loved Jerry, and were absolutely crushed by the news of his death. We were all so devastated." Landers put his hand up to his mouth after speaking in an all too sugary manner.

Geez, I thought. How sickening. Do these people really believe themselves? The banter between Gina and Porter Landers was drowned out by the mental conversation I was having with myself. Who is this guy, the Caligula of Miami? If I tossed this guy into the pool, would he melt? Maybe if I just slammed his head on the metal table. My mental machinations and the conversation was interrupted by the noise of a cart of some type, then by Luke coming into view.

He appeared pushing a cart containing a bucket of ice, a coffee carafe, a pitcher of water, another pitcher of lemonade, along with several clean glasses, cups and silverware. As quickly as he appeared, Luke disappeared back into the estate.

"A choice of beverages for my thirsty friends. We also have the hard stuff if you prefer," Landers said in a whispered tone, touching my arm with his hand. I instinctively pulled my arm back, an action that apparently warranted another soft kick from Gina.

Landers poured himself a glass of lemonade, and both Gina and I selected the same. Real lemon slices fell into our glasses as Gina poured for both of us.

"Mr. Landers, have the Lakewood Police ever contacted you?" I asked.

"No, never, my dear boy." My resentment of his terms of endearment were grating on me like the proverbial nails on a chalkboard.

"Well, perhaps you might shed some insight into Walter's relationship with Jerry, and who Jerry befriended here in Miami. Was he a regular at your club?" I asked.

Landers let out a chuckle at the question about his club. He explained that the club served a class of people with whom they rarely associated. They were above them, or at least that's what I got from his characterizations.

After talking to Landers for nearly two hours, we had seven pages of notes, and consumed a pitcher of lemonade each. More importantly, it all started to become much clearer. Despite his perverse proclivities and flamboyant lifestyle, Landers had a unique tendency to tell the truth. He exposed the good, bad and ugly, and there was little good but plenty of bad and ugly. He provided us with some much needed information that shed light on not only what was taking place in Miami, but in Lakewood as well. Especially in Lakewood.

It was during one of Landers' droning monologues that I picked up on a phrase that was becoming ever so common to our investigation.

He twice referred to the 'yellow brick road' we were traveling to pursue the killer of my uncle. As we would soon learn, we were indeed on a yellow brick road, but not one paved of gold, yet one that would take us to the wizard.

As we left the palatial estate of Porter Landers in our car, we were almost giddy with excitement caused by the information we were able to get from this one interview. He exposed an underworld of debauchery, of pure evil from which he somehow seemingly managed to stay far away. Sordid details punctuated by the absurdly perverse. Past and present, but especially the past.

Carrying a wealth of information in our notebooks, we left the residence. "Let's go back to the room and go over the information and background he gave us, and call Paul to let him know that we're alright." Gina could barely contain her excitement. Neither could I, except that something deep down was nagging at me. This was way too easy, I thought. Unfortunately, I would be proved correct.

CHAPTER 18

Investigatus Interruptus

It was a few minutes before 6:00 p.m. when we arrived back at the hotel. It already had been a long day. A long week. Gina kicked off her high heels and quickly changed back into her shorts and tee-shirt. Meanwhile, I took another trip to the motel bar for a refreshment.

Before sitting down, I put change into the cigarette machine and bought another pack of Marlboros to add to my dwindling supply.

As soon as I sat down at the bar, I placed my order. The bartender poured bourbon straight up and pushed it to me. As I was reaching into my pocket to pay for my drink, the bartender told me that it was already taken care of, compliments of the two gentlemen seated at the table behind me.

Suddenly, I broke into a cold sweat, as the feeling of an evil presence overpowered me.

Before turning around, I downed the drink in one motion, just in case I would not have such an opportunity again.

As it happened, I did not have to turn around. As I placed the empty glass on the bar, the two men flanked me at the bar, each taking a seat on either side of me. I immediately thought of Gina alone in the room.

❖ ❖ ❖

There was a knock on the hotel room door. Gina quickly jumped up to open the door, thinking that I had left my key in the room. Without thinking or looking, she swung open the door, expecting to see me on the other side. It's likely that no one heard her shriek as she was pushed backward into the room by the man in the dark gray business suit wearing aviator sunglasses.

She fell backward onto the bed, and rolled off one bed onto the floor in the space in front of the nightstand that separated the two beds. There, she spotted the shotgun that she had taken from the car. She knew it was empty, but it would be better than nothing. Perhaps it would scare this intruder enough that he would back off.

As she reached for the gun, the well-dressed man stepped on her wrist, pinning it to the floor just inches away from the barrel. She looked up at him from her disadvantaged position on the floor.

"Don't," he said.

❖ ❖ ❖

I called the bartender back over and ordered another bourbon. I lit a cigarette, and blew the smoke in the face of the man to my left. Surprise, surprise. It was an impeccably dressed Porter Landers. To my right was his boy Friday, Luke, who was now dressed in jeans and a dress shirt, although the ancient Egyptian pagan cross was still visible around his neck.

There was a bulge under Luke's shirt, one that was not there because he was happy to see me, either. No, this bulge was obviously made by a gun tucked inside his waistband. Landers opened his sport jacket to reveal the butt of a semi-automatic, held in place by a holster inside the waistband of his dress slacks. In a move I never saw coming, I felt the barrel of his gun against my ribs.

"Marvelous," I uttered.

It's difficult to explain what was going through my mind at this moment. Saying that I was scared witless does not even come close. I was sitting over a thousand miles from my home, surrounded by swamps with alligators, and am being held hostage by two armed members of the homosexual mafia that until my scrape with Walter, showed me great sub-tropical hospitality.

Visions of Gina and I being ushered into the back of a pink

limousine between two of the most flamboyant hit men I've ever seen made me start to laugh. It was a nervous laughter to be sure, but a laugh nonetheless. It is said that laughter is contagious, and it must be, because Landers began laughing with me.

As the bartender brought me my fresh glass of bourbon, I instructed him to take care of my two friends—on me. To my surprise, Landers ordered a drink for himself and his sidekick. I became quite troubled, however, when he addressed the bartender by his first name. Oh this isn't good, I thought. I pretended not to hear, and tried to take the offensive.

"Is he really old enough to drink?" I asked Landers, pointing to Luke on my right.

Landers ignored my question and turned serious. I lit up another cigarette immediately after snuffing out the last.

"You know those will kill you, Marc," chided Landers.

"So I'm told. There are other ways to die, no?" I asked Landers. "By the way, your boy Luke here, do you ever let him talk?" I turned to Luke. "Or is your sugar daddy's hand so far up your rotor-routed ass that he's got hold of your tongue?

"Now Marc, that's no way to talk to your friends." I noticed that Landers no longer possessed the overtly effeminate mannerisms he exhibited at his estate. It was even worse, though, as I noticed something in his eyes. His eyes turned dark, black as night, and his mere presence seemed to create a chill across the bar. My thoughts turned to Gina, alone in the room, not knowing what was taking place less than a hundred feet away. My thoughts then turned a bit darker…Gina!

Instinctively, I crushed my cigarette out and began to stand up, intending to make sure Gina was okay. Luke and Landers both put their hands on my shoulders, pushing me back down in my seat with sufficient force to let me know they meant business.

"We're not done here yet, son," Landers whispered in my ear. I was imagining something similar, or worse, happening to Gina. How could I be so stupid!

Turing to my left, I spoke in the most authoritative voice I could muster, considering I was at a severe disadvantage. "Tell me what's going on, what you want, and then get the hell out of my face."

The bartender brought the drinks for Landers and his sidekick, saying that they were on the house.

"Thanks, Gerard," Landers said to the bartender. "Now I think you've got some stocking to do in the back room." Gerard the bartender quickly walked from behind the otherwise empty bar to a room out of sight. That familiar sick feeling in my stomach was coming back. We certainly did not have the home field advantage.

❖ ❖ ❖

"Stand up, and don't do anything you'll regret, Gina," said the well-dressed uninvited visitor of room 112. He opened his jacket to reveal a semi-automatic pistol hanging from a shoulder holster. Gina complied, rising slowly while rubbing her right wrist, bruised from the force of the man's step.

"Now, walk slowly to the door. Scream and you're dead. Run and you're dead. Do anything other than I tell you, and you're dead."

The man followed Gina to the cement exterior walkway that connected the rooms on the ground floor. "Stand there." The man pointed to what seemed to be an arbitrary spot on the parking lot. The asphalt from the hot Florida sun was burning Gina's feet.

"Can I at least get some shoes on?" she asked.

The man who stood between Gina and the door to the motel room didn't answer. He simply pointed to the spot where she was standing, while placing his hand over the bulge that was the gun under his suit coat.

❖ ❖ ❖

I finished my drink with yet another single motion, pointing to the empty glass suggesting that we get Gerard back. Not so much for another drink, but so he could witness whatever might happen next. Landers pushed my glass into the well of the bar, conveying to me that I was finished here.

"Get up and follow Luke outside. Nice and slow. We're going for a walk. Nice and calm, Marc. Nothing funny."

As I reached the door of the bar, I saw Gina standing barefoot in the parking lot with a deeply concerned look on her face. She kept glancing to her right, telegraphing that someone, or maybe more than one person was just out of my view. Marvelous.

I was happy to see that she appeared alright, although I was all too uncertain about our immediate future. "Walk to Gina and stand there." It was Luke who was giving the orders this time.

"So, he does talk after all," I muttered.

When I reached Gina in the parking lot, she flung her arms around my shoulders and began to cry. "Are you alright, Gina"? I asked.

"She's fine" were the words of an unfamiliar voice coming from the shadows of our motel room.

"So, what are you going to do, Landers, kill us both here in the motel parking lot?" I asked without thinking about the numerous other possibilities that existed. A lot goes through your mind when you are surrounded by bad guys. More when you are outnumbered by bad guys with guns, and they have the home field advantage. Sometimes, like now, words seemed to be falling out of my mouth without much thought behind them. It's nothing like the movies, I thought, where the good guys disarm the bad guys, summon the police and call it a day.

Speaking of police, a marked Miami-Dade County Sheriff's car suddenly pulled into the parking lot where we stood. My hopes were quickly dashed, however, when Landers smiled and waved at the deputy driving the vehicle.

The deputy pulled into the lot and rolled his window down. The car was close enough to all of us that I felt the cooler air from the car's interior waft across my now very clammy skin.

"Marshall! We're just finishing up here," Landers said to the deputy.

"Need any help? Are we gonna need a clean-up on aisle six?" asked the deputy, laughing with Landers and Luke, who now joined the frivolities. I began to laugh too, nervously, but to show them that I was unafraid and at that moment, unbalanced.

"What are you laughing about, Stiles?" The deputy sheriff's face seemed to contort into a rubber version of its former appearance.

"You bunch of fruitcakes. I'm laughing at you dickless bunch of homos," I said, wishing afterward that I kept my mouth shut. After all, we were playing in their sandbox. Thinking our predicament through, I regained my senses and decided to stop talking.

Gina and I looked at each other, knowing that we were in a den of lions. Mere seconds passed when the deputy rolled up his window and made a U-turn in the near empty parking lot of the motel. He beeped his horn as he left the motel, his tires squealing on the hot asphalt as he turned onto the road.

"Get inside." Landers pointed to our room and instructed Gina and I away from the empty shotgun. Once the door shut behind him, Luke and the other visitor were no longer to be seen. "Sit down and listen."

Perhaps it was because I was a bit more relaxed from the bourbon, or maybe I just liked the odds a bit better, I started to voice my objections from my seat at the table by the window while mentally contemplating how I could get my hands on the shotgun.

Not amused, Landers unbuttoned his coat while I simultaneously received another under-the-table kick from Gina. Landers started laughing. "You should learn to take a hint from the pretty lady."

Landers began his soliloquy with the statement, "There are a lot worse things than death. You're not going to die today, well, at least I'm not going to kill you, or have you killed. You're going to leave town now, and not come back. For the sake of your son and daughter Marc, and for your daughter, Gina, you're going to go back to Lakewood and stop sticking your noses into places they don't belong. As you can tell, I've got a lot of friends here, and you're making them uncomfortable."

For another five minutes, Landers continued his lecture to his captive audience. My mind was racing, and I quietly considered rushing the man as he again became deeply immersed in his own words. Bad idea, as I have no clue where his personal attendants were, or if the police would even be able to sort out the mess, or would even want to, considering the cozy relationship with the deputy sheriff. No, I'll just shut up for once. After all, a man must know his limitations.

As it turned out, listening and giving the outward appearance of complete cooperation had its benefits. Landers had actually added to the information he provided earlier in the day. He seemed to be in some type of trance made by the sound of his own voice, which oddly took on a German accent. It was almost like watching a pornographic movie, I thought, wondering if or when the scene would reach its completion. It was surreal.

After making sure that we understood that we were to leave the motel, and the county forthwith, Landers and his merry young men disappeared as quickly as they appeared. Gina and I sat there motionless for several minutes, unsure of exactly what just happened.

After a few minutes of mindless discussion, we gathered up our things and loaded them into the car. Across the parking lot was a shiny black Mercedes backed into one of the spots across from our room. We could easily see two men occupying the front seat. An uneasiness gripped both of us. Even the shotgun did not give us much hope against the forces of darkness that were so pervasive all around us.

I was nursing the knot on my head where Houghton got in a sucker punch, and Gina was gently holding and rubbing her wrist where the gay mafia goon had kept it solidly against the floor. We felt battered, beaten and exhausted, but glad to leave this sub-tropical sewage behind us.

I pulled up to the motel office and returned our keys.

"Oh, you're checking out already?" asked the young female clerk. "Was everything alright?" she asked quizzically. For a brief second, I felt like telling her about my stay, including the servitude of the bartender to the capo of a homosexual mafia that apparently held her paradise hostage. My mind changed when I saw the Mercedes inching toward the bumper of my car.

"Fine, it's all good," I said rather nervously. "We had an emergency arise and we can't stay. Thanks for your hospitality." I left without bothering to take a receipt.

I slipped behind the wheel and inched the car up to the street. After making sure it was clear both ways, well, except for a box truck that was barreling down to our left, I floored it, leaving a trail of rubber and smoke from the rear tires. I watched as the Mercedes started to pull out right behind us, although the sound of the brakes locking up on the box truck apparently changed the driver's mind. The driver shoved the Mercedes in reverse, backing up several precious feet to avoid a certain collision. Pleased with myself, I found the on ramp to the interstate and began traveling north. Gina let out a big sigh of relief as we sped through the traffic toward the county line.

It took about an hour, or about 70 miles before either of us could talk in complete sentences. By then, we had lost our escort and put Dade County behind us, with the buffer of another county in between.

"Hungry?" I asked Gina.

"No, but we should eat. We've got a lot to talk about, Marc, we've got a lot to sort out. We probably should find someplace to stay tonight to rest up for our trip back north," Gina added.

"Let's treat ourselves to a nice hotel with room service," I suggested. "We can order in and go over the case."

❖ ❖ ❖

It was dark by the time we reached West Palm Beach and found a clean and nicely appointed hotel with late night room service near the interstate. By most standards, the hotel of our choice was upscale, catering to businessmen and families. We considered it a treat, a well-deserved luxury we had yet to experience in this southern journey.

We did our best to make certain we were not followed, although carried the shotgun with us into the hotel room just to be safe. We hid it inside a garment bag with our other luggage. Neither of us were going to venture out of the room tonight. As planned, we ordered room service, which consisted of a large carafe of coffee and some light late-night fare.

We ate in relative silence at the over-sized wooden table close to the window overlooking a nicely decorated and well-lit courtyard, still trying to shake off the events of the day. We were both mentally and physically exhausted.

After finishing our meal, Gina called home to talk with her daughter. "All is well on the home front," she said to me after hanging up the phone. "Think we should call Paul?" she asked.

After considering the lateness of the hour, I decided against it. After all, Paul was probably busy with his security work or long asleep, I reasoned. "Anyway, he would have contacted us on our beepers with anything important," I said.

Gina paused and exhibited a quizzical look, then began searching her purse and other cases we had brought to the room. Then a small suitcase. "I left mine in Lakewood. Did you bring yours?" she asked.

"No, it's still in my desk drawer," I replied. "The thing's a pain."

After a few minutes of consideration, I tried to call Paul anyway, but received the answering service instead. According to the service, Paul was out on a late night security detail. I left a generic message, giving the service the name and number to our hotel. Unless there was an emergency, I added, I would talk to him in the morning.

"Marc, don't you have anyone else you want to call?" Gina pressed. I chuckled and shook my head, feeling as alone as I've ever felt. "No, not now," was my answer as I considered the black hole my life had become.

Our plans to discuss the case in detail lost out against our physical exhaustion and pain. We laid on our respective beds in silence. It wasn't long before sleep overcame the both of us. It was the kind of sleep that was the product of complete mental and physical exhaustion.

CHAPTER 19

Thursday, May 14, 1987

I awoke with a start, jerking myself up in bed while trying to focus on anything around me. Nothing but darkness and silence, except for a thin, horizontal sliver of light under the door to my left. My mouth was parched and I was disoriented. The side of my head was throbbing and I was desperately trying to orient myself.

I turned my head and saw the time illuminated on the clock radio was 5:07. It took me another few seconds to realize that I was in a hotel room in West Palm Beach, Florida, and it was just after five in the morning on Thursday. Rubbing the side of my head, I felt a lump that was the result of my encounter with Walter Houghton less than 24 hours ago. Memories of the last few days began flood into the recesses of my brain like a tsunami. I laid back down on my pillow to give myself a chance to mentally process the events of the last few days.

As my bare back and neck hit the sheet and pillow, I could feel their dampness from my own sweat. Now that I was somewhat acclimated to the darkness, I turned my head to the right to account for Gina in the other bed. I was able to make out her silhouette by the light coming from under the door.

After spending several minutes mentally rehashing all of the information we uncovered from our encounters thus far, I decided to get up and prepare for the day ahead.

Dressed only in my boxers and socks, I quietly slipped from under the sheet and began my trek in the darkness to the bathroom for a much needed and well deserved shower. I felt like the Pink Panther as I tip toed to avoid waking Gina. As I turned the corner to the bathroom, my leg landed squarely against the room service cart we had brought in last night. The noise shattered the quiet and I lost my balance. As I tried desperately not to fall, I tipped the cart, causing the metal carafe and all of the dishes to crash to the floor.

As if summoned by unseen forces, the room suddenly lit up from the lantern style lights on the wall and I heard the unmistakable sound of a shell being racked in the chamber of a shotgun. I instinctively froze.

"Shit, Marc, you scared the crap out of me. What in the hell are you doing? Are you alright? Are you sleepwalking? What time is it? I could have shot you, you know!" Gina's questions and assurance that I could have been killed came in rapid bursts. The stress in her voice was as evident as the genuine fright in mine. "Sorry, Gina, go back to sleep. I was just headed for the bathroom."

I looked back at her as she lowered the shotgun and pointed it down and away from me. She removed the round from the chamber as she mumbled various expletives to herself, interrupting her tirade long enough to ask whether she could turn the lights back off. "Please, it's early, just after five, get some more rest," I said, and apologized again for startling her.

I turned on the bathroom light, which provided enough light for me to place the room service cart upright and put the carafe and dishes on the top tray. Now very much awake, I made my way into the bathroom and shut the door.

As I stood under the tepid water in the shower, I wondered how many people begin their day in this fashion. I spent a long time soaping and scrubbing the sweat and grime that accumulated since my last shower. I wore the motel soap down to half of its original size in my attempt to scrub away the depravity and perversion I encountered the previous day. Despite my best attempts, it didn't work.

About a half hour later, I exited the bathroom fully dressed except for my tie and suit coat. The room was still dark, and I marveled at how Gina could just go back to sleep after being so abruptly awakened. It was then I noticed that her bed was empty and her room key was gone from the nightstand. The car keys, however, were still in the room. For a few seconds, I was overcome by a deep fear, not knowing what happened to Gina.

As I turned on the room lights and opened the curtain, the door to our room swung open. Gina was carrying a cardboard tray with two extra-large cups of coffee from the 24-hour diner adjacent to the motel. "I figured we could both use a better way to wake up," she said, and placed the coffee on the table by the window. "Anyway, I needed to use the bathroom and it didn't seem like you were coming out anytime soon."

Gina grabbed her coffee and small travel bag and walked to the bathroom. "My turn," she said as she disappeared behind the door. I placed the room service cart into the hallway and turned on the television, tuning it to CNN.

I caught up on the news I missed over the last few days, and watched a video clip of some senator talking about the growing Iran-Contra scandal. I muted the television after a few minutes and turned my attention to the pages of notes spread across the table. I lit up a cigarette and settled in with my coffee. It was during my time of trying to wash away the utter darkness I felt that Gina had separated our notes in neat stacks atop the table.

I was so involved in the paperwork that I almost didn't notice that Gina had taken the seat across from me. When I looked up at her, I noticed that she was frowning while studying one page from our notes very carefully. "What's up, Gina?" I asked.

"Nothing make sense, Marc."

My mind raced to stitch together certain facts we had uncovered on our trip and combine them with information we had before we left.

"What in the hell did we stumble into?" I asked. "Nobody down here could have done the murder, at least not according to the evidence, but they certainly don't seem too innocent, either."

"Right, so now let's think outside of the box," Gina said very slowly. "Let's start from the very beginning. We've gotta take a few steps back and look at the bigger picture."

"C'mon Gina, it's not even seven o'clock in the morning, my head hurts, I'm tired and we're a thousand miles from home. Not only that, you almost shot me this morning!" I could hear myself whining, and it didn't sound very appealing. Catching myself, I changed my tone and delivery and asked her what she was thinking. She suddenly became very animated.

"Let's establish what we know. Just the basics, for now. Lakewood PD obviously has the prints of the person who killed Jerry. Evidence carved in stone, ah, well, at least stained in blood. They don't have a murder weapon, but it was obviously a knife. All of the knives were accounted for in your dad's kitchen, so the murder weapon was apparently brought in by the killer," Gina said.

"So?" I replied, although following along.

"So, all they need is a person to match with the prints."

"Tell me something I don't know," I interjected.

"The cops told us that they checked the alibis of everybody we talked to in Miami, even their cabana boys or whatever you call them, and they all have solid alibis. Apparently, though, at least according to Landers, they didn't. Yet, everybody in Jerry's known circle of friends has been ruled out by the forensic evidence."

"Okay, go on."

"So those are the basic facts, or at least the facts as they were presented to us in the form of police reports, right?"

"Right," I stipulated.

"What if they're lying?" Gina asked. "Somebody is definitely lying. What if someone *on the inside* of this investigation is gaming us? After all, aren't you the least bit curious about how everybody seemed to know that we were coming? I mean, there was no surprise at all."

"Well, it did make the news and the newspaper, thanks to Paul."

"Yes, but the news was just a week old. Think about that for a little bit. It's like there's a WATS line of information, a pipeline from Lakewood to Miami. It doesn't seem to fit the pattern of normal conversation by people just relaying information during the course of casual conversations. It feels more organized. It has to be. And I think it's got to be coming from someone on the inside."

"The inside of what?"

"The inside of either the police or the D.A.'s office. Maybe the paper, too. Any of them. Or, maybe all of them."

"Go on," I prompted.

"Let's just start from the beginning. First, with as much evidence that was left at the scene, Lakewood PD said it would be an open and shut case. Detective McCarty told you they'd probably solve the case in a day or two, tops, remember that?"

"Sure, but it's not like television. I mean, things happen, or in this case, don't happen."

"I know, but I was reading the notes of your meetings with the Lakewood Police and the county district attorney when you notified them of our trip. Did anything strike you as being a bit strange, or off, when you told them we were coming down here?"

As I carefully contemplated my answer, Gina began prompting me with more questions.

"When you told Mack—Detective McCarty that we were coming down to Florida, what did he say? How about the district attorney, what did he have to say?" asked Gina.

"I remember the meeting with the district attorney very well. Paul and I went down to the courthouse and let him know in person. Paul said that we would be coming down here now, I mean this week. He laughed at first and then said that it would be a waste of our time. Then he seemed to get irritated when we reaffirmed our plans of coming down here. He spent a few minutes lecturing us on spending our client's—my family's money. His demeanor did change. He said that he was going to tell Chief Deitz about our trip. Yet, he was adamant about finding the killer. He seemed to want the case closed."

"You sensed a conflict, right?"

"I suppose. There seemed to be no problem with finding the killer, just so we did not disturb anyone else in the process."

"And there it is," said Gina.

"There what is, Gina? I asked, overcome by the need for more caffeine and an overwhelming desire to get on the road for home.

"I think I can explain." Sensing my edginess, Gina suggested that we stay put a little longer to review her theory amid the evidence we had. "Nobody knows where we're at, so we can use a bit of time to rethink things. Let's call room service one last time before we leave. Let's take this opportunity away from everything to review my theory for the next few hours or so. No interruptions. It's still early, and we can check out and probably be home before office hours tomorrow."

Knowing better than to second guess her investigative instincts, I picked up the hotel phone, dialed room service and after asking what she wanted to eat, ordered coffee and Eggs Benedict for both of us. We were going to stop to eat on our way back anyway, so why not just do it now, and even splurge a little, I thought.

While waiting for room service, we moved the shotgun out of sight from potentially prying hotel employee eyes and packed our bags, setting each by the door. We used Gina's bed as a makeshift table for my briefcase and spread the contents over the bedspread, while using the table to write notes and organize various papers and notes.

Twenty minutes after I hung up the hotel phone, there was a knock at the door. I opened the door and a young man pushed the cart into the room, instructing me to place the cart into the hallway next to the one from the previous night when we were finished. I charged the breakfast to the room and handed him a few bucks for his trouble.

❖ ❖ ❖

We settled in at the table with our plates of eggs, fresh fruit and extra muffins, which represented a dramatic change from my normal fare of cold pizza and bad coffee. It actually felt nice for once to share a good meal with someone who has become a close friend under such unusual circumstances.

For the first time in a long time, I felt more relaxed, despite the events of the last few days and the rush I experienced earlier this morning. Instead of talking about the murder, we found ourselves talking about our personal lives as we finished our breakfast together. It was a time of bonding. I suddenly looked at her as a woman and not just a fellow detective or a partner in the field. We talked about her daughter, her past, and her present situation. It was during this conversation that I saw the soft, womanly side of her. She shared her vulnerabilities with me, and I with her. We found ourselves gazing out the window at the palm trees and areas of sand across the courtyard.

We talked about our experiences with life, love and death. We shared our most frightening moments—our individual brushes with death.

I recalled a day in June of 1978. I completed my training as a firefighter in one of the country's most respected fire schools a few weeks earlier, and was assigned to an engine company that covered a heavily populated residential and commercial area. We got a call for a structure fire at a split-level single family residence. I was riding in one jump seat while Russ, the paramedic who responded to my father's house the day my dad found my uncle dead, occupied the other.

As we approached the scene, the captain pounded on the window behind me, and motioned me and Russ to "mask up." We strapped the heavy air tanks on our backs and pulled the full face masks over our heads, replacing our fire helmets after turning the valves that regulated the air flow to our masks. I unhooked my fire coat and placed my eyeglasses into my shirt pocket. At the same time, Russ and I gave the captain a "thumbs up." The engine slowed so Ernie, who was riding on the tail board, could jump off and wrap the fire hose around the closest hydrant. We turned our heads to see a large, black plume of smoke rising about a hundred feet in front of us.

As we pulled up, Russ and I simultaneously jumped down from the rig and grabbed the fire hose. Russ took the nozzle position, and I slid behind him. Within seconds, the captain had connected the hose to the pump and the hose became charged, turning it from a limp, flat canvas into an angry, highly pressurized snake.

We were just a few feet from the front door, preparing entry into a room consumed by fire. Just then, I heard a loud bang, louder than anything I've ever heard in my life. Before the noise stopped, I felt the tank attached to Russ' back strike me squarely in my chest, followed by all 200 pounds of Russ and the extra 75 pounds of his equipment sending me backwards. We were both lifted off of our feet and ended up laying side by side about ten feet from the front door, looking skyward as pieces of wood and asphalt from the roof rained down upon us. At first, I thought it was a back draft, but we were told later that a gas line ruptured and was spewing natural gas into the front part of the house. Another few seconds and we would have been inside, and the outcome would likely have been much worse.

It was still bad. The blast knocked Russ right out of his boots, both of which remained in an oddly peculiar position on the stoop in front of the now-widened doorway. It blew both of our helmets from our heads and the heat singed our hair and eyebrows, and knocked the wind out of both of us. We each suffered concussions, cuts, bad bruises and could not hear very well for a day or two. I never did find my eyeglasses, which somehow made their way out of my coat, sailing on a skyward trajectory. But we were alive.

Gina told me about her call to a domestic dispute one dark night in the late fall of that same year—1978. A husband was threatening his wife, but his wife failed to tell the dispatcher that he was armed with a .357 Magnum. Gina arrived and entered the house at the invitation of the wife. Just then, the husband appeared from the hallway, carrying a loaded .357 magnum in his right hand.

"I don't think there was 8 feet between us," Gina said. "He didn't say a word. He just lifted the gun to chest height and fired at me. The bullet struck the wall behind me." Gina paused momentarily and stared into space.

"The investigators figured that it traveled between my right arm and body as I was reaching for my service weapon. It was a fluke. One inch made the difference between me being here and *not* being here. He only fired one shot and dropped his gun. I drew down on him, but by that time he had dropped his gun. I was milliseconds away from dispatching him from this earth. It all happened so fast. After I had him cuffed, their little girl ran from her bedroom crying at the sound of the gunshot. When she saw her dad lying on the floor, she screamed," she said.

"It was later that night that I noticed a horizontal tear in my uniform shirt, midway between my armpit and my waist. My shirt was bloused out, and the slug ripped through the material. I never felt it." Tears began to well in Gina's eyes.

"I took the next few days off. I could not get the thought of how close I came to dying that day out of my head. Or killing someone else. I still remember the face of the little girl, holding her stuffed animal, running to her mother and clutching her mother's leg. She was about the same age as my daughter was at that time. I knew then I had to find another profession, not just for me, but for my daughter. Of course, that decision was made for me."

We continued to exchange stories and even showing our scars from battles past, talking about how much death we had seen between us so early in our lives. Death in all different forms. From natural, peaceful deaths to the most hideous imaginable. Gunshots, stabbings, hangings, decapitations from auto accidents.

We talked about our families and our mutual estrangements under different circumstances. We talked about our dreams and our disappointments, the occasional good times wedged between the long stretches of heartaches. We talked about loneliness. We talked until there seemed to be no words left to describe our feelings.

"You know, we should probably be in some form of mental health counseling," Gina said, laughing at us comparing notes of the morbid scenes we've encountered over the years and our feelings of heartache from so many other sources.

"Maybe we could get a discount if we used the buddy system," I chided.

Our muted laughter turned to silence as we both became lost in our past. Gina placed her hand on my right arm, turned her head away and looked out the window. I could see a tear well up in her eye and fall down her cheek. It struck the plate on the table below her.

I put my left hand on hers and squeezed tightly, saying nothing as there was nothing to say. We remained motionless for at least a minute. She used her free hand to wipe her eyes, stood up and stepped around the table, sitting on the edge of her bed after pushing aside some papers, facing me as I continued to sit in the chair. I turned toward her, studying the heartache and anguish present in her face. She placed her hands on my knees and bowed her head. She began to sob.

I stood up and pulled her to me, hugging her gently as she buried her head in my neck. It was a moment of genuine compassion for each other. It was one of life's sudden and unexpected intermissions—a moment of emotional disorder caused when fear, loneliness and intense, unspeakable heartache felt by one person intersects the same of another. It took no time for my own tears to moisten the tufts of her light brown hair that rested on top of her shoulder. Our embrace lasted until our tears stopped and our fears, at least for now, were allayed by the comfort of each other's grasp.

Without speaking, Gina slipped from our embrace and walked into the bathroom, closing the door behind her. In the emptiness I felt, I simply moved the room service cart into the hallway, leaving the carafe of coffee and our cups on the table. I returned to my seat and lit a cigarette, watching the morning breeze rustle the palm fronds as I peered out the window.

Having dried her eyes and repaired her makeup, Gina joined me at the table and lit a cigarette that she took from my pack. Our eyes locked again, but we sat in silence as neither one of us knew how to reach beyond the emptiness we felt. We had brought ourselves to the emotional abyss caused by life and death, fear and heartache that few will understand and even fewer will ever experience. About that… we were just out of words.

❖ ❖ ❖

The sun's rays penetrated the room, illuminating the smoke formations above the table. I opened the window and moist, salty air wafted into the room by a gentle breeze. The fresh air seemed to renew our senses and enhanced our ability to focus on the task at hand. We continued where we left off before breakfast and before our emotional interlude temporarily sidetracked us.

Gina spoke first. "There is something really evil taking place all around us, Marc, and it's beginning to scare me. I think it's something that we just stumbled into, some sort of perverted, sadistic, ritualistic underground sex club that your uncle seems to have encountered."

"That seems about right," I said.

"Remember our meeting with Paul? Well, I took some time to look through all of the old papers and clippings from your uncle. One cover paper had a symbol on it. It was an Ankh, as you said. Looking closer at every scrap of paper, I found *another* symbol. This one was a circle with what looked like a star inside. Here it is," she said as she showed me a third or fourth generation copy.

"At first I didn't think much of it. But then I did some research at the library and found out what it really was."

"Which is, what?"

"Well, wait. You remember the guy that came into our room and pushed me down. Well, I noticed something yesterday that he was wearing. It was a gold necklace of what I thought was a star inside of a circle as well. It was the exact same symbol.

"Symbol of what?" I asked again, a bit more insistently.

"It's an ancient symbol of Baphomet. A goat's head. The devil."

"Are you sure?"

"Quite sure, and I wish I wasn't."

"So two different symbols, both demonic in nature. What is this, a perverted devil worship sex club we've found?" I asked.

"Marc, I think so. I think we are working two different cases.

Paul was correct from the start. He just did not know how right he was. Or did he?" Gina's voice trailed off.

Gina continued her narrative. We were both going through the exercise of mentally connecting various dots as she spoke.

"The thing that has stuck in my mind is that you keep comparing your uncle's behavior to what was shown in the movie *Looking For Mr. Goodbar*. I think you're right. I think Jerry and Walter split up, and Jerry became reckless, *or because he became reckless*, living exactly like his female counterpart in that movie. That fits his pattern of behavior. The murder itself was a frenzied killing. In the middle of a sexual encounter. Or before. Or after. Or maybe the word I should use is 'and.' Regardless, no normal or sane person would kill like that. The sicko who did it would certainly kill again, unless he was dead or in prison, don't you think?"

"I suppose," I muttered, trying to determine where Gina was taking us.

"No! Unless he has and it's been covered up. We are still thinking inside the box!" Gina exclaimed.

"How many more hints and clues do we need? It's right in front of our faces, and the very people we've encountered are laughing at us for not seeing what's going on," she added. "That's why they didn't kill us when they had the chance. Once they find out that we know, well, then it will be a different story," she said, watching for my reaction.

"Maybe it's the hit on my head, Gina, or maybe I'm just a bad student. I'm still not following you." I lit another cigarette and poured more coffee for both of us.

"I guess I've been kind of holding out on you, Marc. Right before we left, I did a lot of research at the library of the symbol Martin Tingsley gave us. I also looked into the goat head symbol from one of Jerry's papers, the one everybody seemed to miss or not pay much attention to. I also called my former supervisor when I was a cop. I asked him to access recent and historical FBI crime statistics in our area for all sexual crimes, child abductions, and satanic ritual abuse crimes. I didn't really want to dump all of my findings on you, as I did not want to muddy the waters unnecessarily. But now I think it's time."

Gina continued, "I also omitted something from my report about Cooper, partly because I wasn't sure. When we were in the car together, I saw that he was wearing a gold necklace—"

"Let me guess," I interrupted. "It was a cross, or Ankh, right?".

"Nope. It was a goat's head. The symbol of Baphomet. The very same symbol contained in your uncle's papers."

"But aside from that one instance in his papers from decades ago, and unless I'm missing something, none of this seems to have anything to do with the murder of my uncle. Or does it?" I asked.

"This symbolism, or more accurately, the activity represented by it is the nexus point of our two seemingly different investigations," Gina insisted.

Perhaps it was the warm breeze coming into the room through the window, or the change of scenery from the grayish brown of Lakewood to the lush green opulence of our current location. Whatever the reason, everything was becoming much clearer to me at that moment. I could tell that Gina felt the same, as we both made a mad rush to grab papers from different folders we had arranged for our Florida investigation. I lifted the folder labeled Benjamin Cooper from the stack of papers that surrounded us. We looked each other in the eyes, knowing that we were finally putting pieces of this most intricate puzzle together. It was that elusive 'aha' moment that we were both searching for, but seemed just out of reach.

Both of us began speaking at the same time, then abruptly stopped at the same time to give the other the floor. "You first," Gina said.

"For starters, it's something I found in the background of Benjamin Cooper that I thought was merely a computer error. You know how often we get different names associated with someone's social security number which is usually the result of sloppy work by some clerk somewhere. I initially chalked it up to 'computer litter,' or meaningless erroneous information about Cooper. Now, based on your observation of Cooper wearing that necklace and the image in my uncle's papers, combined with what we've seen down here, I think we've caught a break. If I'm right, if we're right, I'm not certain I like where this case is headed."

"I saw that other name for Cooper in the printout," Gina said. "That's exactly where I was going too."

I laid the pages from the background check on Benjamin Cooper across the bed next to the table. We both focused on the cover page that listed Cooper's social security number and 'aliases." Under aliases, there were multiple variations of Cooper's name, from Ben Cooper, to numerous spelling variations of his first name and middle initial. Among the names, however, one in particular stood out from the rest: Rudolph Fleischer.

Looking deeper into the mundane information, we both agreed that there's not a lot of historical background on Benjamin Cooper.

Too little, in fact for a man of 64 years. He's married to a woman 15 years his junior, a successful businessman and wealthy. There are huge gaps in his professional resume. And then, of course, the other name on the printout. "Both names match in age and other identifying information, which is not as common as one might think if it was merely a clerical error, though. My research concluded that Cooper, or Fleischer, whatever the case might be, is originally from Germany," Gina said.

"Yet somehow, he is associated with my uncle through the U.S. Army during Korea. It doesn't make sense, which is the reason I originally dismissed it. Additionally, he's been a long time and well-known resident of Lakewood. He runs with the rich and powerful."

"And don't forget Landers' speech, and the way his German accent seemed to emerge as he talked when he was in a near trance-like state," I said, tossing it out for relevance.

"I noticed that too. Landers is in the same age group and I'll bet his profile mirrors Cooper's as well."

"Marc, you dismissed the Cooper alias because it didn't make sense, and it didn't to me either. Until I remembered something that had to do with a case I worked on as a cop. It was almost ten years ago, and I didn't connect the names until now. I'm sorry Marc."

"For what Gina? For not remembering every name from every case you ever worked?" I said, trying to be reassuring.

"This case was different. A lot different."

"How so? Tell me about it."

"I will, but first I need to ask you a question. Marc, do you believe in God?"

"Of course I do, Gina. You know I graduated from a seminary in my 'previous' life," I said, straining to lighten the mood.

"Then you believe that Satan exists, too."

"Of course I do. I believe in good and evil, God and the devil, heaven and hell, and the Bible. I just don't wear it on my sleeve, and I'll admit that I'm not a model Christian. I'm working on that and I have a long way to go, but I do believe. Why?"

"It was in May of 1978, about a month before my close encounter with death I told you about. I got a call to respond to investigate the welfare of a child. His name was Todd, and he was a young boy who turned ten years old the week before the call. I arrived at the dilapidated residence where a husband and wife were living with their four young children. The place was filthy, and the kids were dirty and unkempt. A neighbor reported that Todd showed up to play with her son, and she saw bruises on his arms and scratches on his chest. When I got to the house, two of the children, one of them Todd, were playing in the front yard."

Gina began to tear up, turning away from me and looking out the window.

"Although everything on the surface seemed to check out okay, except for the dirt and grit that seems to accompany poverty, I could feel that something was wrong, but I could not put my finger on it. As soon as I stepped out of my cruiser, Todd and his brother looked afraid. But it was not like a normal fear. It was a deep fear that seemed to push him into an almost catatonic state. He stood up but seemed paralyzed by me," Gina said.

"No sooner than I got out of my car, Todd's father rushed out of the house and immediately stood by him and his brother. He was quick to ask why I was there and whether the boys said anything to me. I told him that I was checking on a report that his son might have been injured, as he had been seen with deep scratches on his chest by a few of the neighbors."

"He's fine. Tell her son, that you're fine," the father insisted. "I began to get uneasy, and told the father that I would prefer to hear it from his son."

"The boy's father looked at his son, almost staring through him. Todd then told me that he had been playing on the swing set out back and fell from the swing when his brother pushed him too high, scraping his chest and bruising his arms."

"Mind if I take a look?" I asked.

"He asked me if I had a warrant, and I told him that I did not need one. I also told him I would get a warrant if he chose not to cooperate, but it would encompass much more than checking out Todd. Almost reluctantly, he told his son to show me his injuries from his fall."

"Marc, he had bruises to his arms and chest that could have been from a rough fall from the swing. But it was a small blood stain near the back pocket of his jeans, on his backside, that concerned me the most. When I asked him about the blood, the boy said that he wiped his hand, which had blood on it, on his pants. His father chimed in right away, saying 'like boys do.' It seemed plausible, but I was not entirely convinced. After I did as much as I could at the scene, I immediately returned to the station and filed a report with the officer in charge. I also recommended that children services be notified and conduct a more thorough and complete investigation.

"So you followed SOP, Gina, what else could you do?" I reassured her, suspecting that there was more to come. I was correct, there was more.

"About three weeks later, a young boy who occasionally played with Todd went missing. He's still missing to this day, to my knowledge. I inserted myself into the investigation which was being handled by the State Police, but they were less than receptive to anything I had to offer. The whole situation stunk, Marc. The feds were called in, and that's when things took a really weird turn. I happened to be dating one of the detectives who worked for the State Police. He let me accompany him to a wooded area about 300 yards from Todd's house, acting on a tip from a hiker."

Gina nervously lit a cigarette and finished the remaining coffee, now cold, from her cup.

"What I saw there was like something out of a horror movie. There was a shallow pit and the dirt was caked with dried blood, which was later determined to be from an animal. There was a lot of hair, which the lab said came from a German Shepherd. There were Pentagrams etched into the trees. It now reminds me of the star, the Baphomet jewelry worn by Cooper and the other guy down here. There was a makeshift altar, for sacrifices, as it appeared. It was unreal," Gina said.

"Sounds like it. But what does all of this have to do with the young boy who you were called to check on, other than social and geographical proximity?" I asked.

"Todd was later interviewed by investigators about the missing boy. Of course, his father was present, and ran interference every step of the way. I don't recall how, but investigators determined that Todd's father was familiar with that place in the woods and leaned on him. His story was that his German Shepherd had gone missing, and he happened to find that place while looking for his 'lost' dog. But he never mentioned the animal remains, nor did he seem upset about it. None of it made sense to me at the time, but I was essentially told to butt out as the case was under federal jurisdiction. Everything went into a black hole, and none of the information I just told you was ever reported."

"Let me get this straight," I said. "Todd's father's dog goes missing, and while searching for it, he finds this spot in the woods but never says anything to anyone, and didn't seem disturbed about what he saw. Then a hiker comes along, and being upset at what he sees, calls the police. Meanwhile, a young boy went missing from the same area, a playmate of Todd, and is still missing. And evidence of satanic worship is kept hidden from the public."

"That about sums it up," Gina said.

"Was there any evidence of human remains found at this location?"

"I don't think so. At least not that I heard. The State Police notified the FBI, and the entire thing went dark. The feds had the area dozed over."

'Who was the child?' I asked.

"His name is Lucas Manning. I still have some notes about it packed away at home. I remember that there was a nasty custody dispute that involved the boy, and there were rumors within the department that the boy's maternal grandparents might have taken the boy out of state. At least that was the 'hopeful' suspicion at the time, which seemed to stifle a lot of panic back then. That place in the woods really got to me, but it didn't seem to fit anywhere in the disappearance case."

"And how do you think it fits now, Gina?"

"I didn't make the connection until I rechecked the background report on Benjamin Cooper. The land where this sacrificial plot was found is owned by Rudolph Fleischer."

"One and the same, you think?"

"No question about it, in my mind."

"We need to speak to Cooper, and find out the disposition of the missing child case," I said.

"Why don't you call the office just to let Paul know that we're okay," Gina said. Little did we know, the case of my uncle's murder and everything in its orbit was about to take yet another dark turn.

❖ ❖ ❖

I picked up the phone on the nightstand between the beds as I removed my long distance calling card from my wallet. Annie answered on the first ring. I could sense urgency in her voice as she said that Paul needed to talk to us right away.

Before turning the phone over to Paul, she said that Mary Tingsley called our office yesterday, insisting that she and Martin meet with us right away. Annie said that she told her that we were in Florida and would be returning in a few days. Probing for more information, she got Mary to admit that Martin had not told us everything during our first meeting, and said that Martin has something he wants to give us, now that he feels that he can trust us.

I asked Annie if Mary disclosed what it was that he wanted us to have. She said that despite her best attempts, Mary refused to disclose anything, except to me or Gina. I asked Annie to call Mary and tell her that we spoke, and assure her that we would call them as soon as we got back and meet right away. Annie then called Paul to the phone.

"How soon can you two get back here, Marc?" Paul asked with a level of concern I've rarely heard from him.

"Why, what's wrong? Annie already told us about Martin," I said with authority.

"Benjamin Cooper is dead."

"What? How?" I pressed.

"Well, the official story is that he killed himself at his house. His wife found him in his den, the room that he used as his office when she got home from shopping. Shot once in the head. His wife swears that he did not own a gun, but a .45 Glock was found at the scene. The gun was traced back to a retired Lakewood cop who reported it stolen in 1980. I'm working on getting more information."

I felt a sudden dryness grip my throat and mouth. My mind raced as I stood silent, trying to mentally file this new development in its appropriate spot.

"When did this happen?" I asked

"His wife says she found him yesterday afternoon around 5:30, so sometime before that."

Gina could see the change in my demeanor and quickly moved by my side, motioning for me to give her an update. "Cooper is dead" was all I could whisper to Gina. It was all I really needed to say. The news caused her to take a quick step backward and fall to a sitting position on the bed. Her reaction was one of shock, disbelief and concern.

Paul continued his update, "Cooper's wife called here, looking for you or Gina. I talked to her. She said that two Lakewood detectives came before the coroner even got there and went through his desk and all of his belongings, like they were on a scavenger hunt," Paul continued. They took a bunch of stuff without asking, and even opened a combination safe Cooper had in his office."

"How did they manage that? Did they pry it open? I asked.

"No, they told his wife that they found the combination under his desk blotter, but she insisted that he never kept the combination anywhere near his desk."

"What did they take?"

"Well, she said that they kept her in the kitchen, but she could see them take papers, pictures, and film. They didn't touch gold coins and some very expensive jewelry, including a Rolex," said Paul.

Not expecting an answer, I asked to no one in particular, "What the hell is going on?"

"Just get back here as soon as you can, and drive carefully, if you know what I mean," Paul cautioned. "And since you two decided to leave your pagers here, call in every few hours or so." Paul hung up without saying anything else.

Although Gina heard most of the conversation, I filled in the blanks as she sat at the table, lighting another cigarette. Suddenly, she began searching the papers until she came upon the complete background report on Benjamin Cooper that included his complete personal and professional history. Gina seemed transfixed on one page of the report that listed information about his wife and extended family. After a few minutes, she lifted her head from the papers and looked at me as if she was trying to calculate the answer of a complex math problem.

"What's up, Gina?"

"Damn it, Marc, why didn't I see this before?" she said with obvious frustration. I don't believe for a minute that Cooper killed himself, Marc. Somebody wanted him dead. And somebody is looking for something, and I'm wondering if whoever 'they' are, think I… we might have what they're looking for," Gina said.

"Go on," I urged.

"It's Sadie Cooper, his wife. Her maiden name is Manning, the same last name as Lucas, the boy who went missing. I know that she is not Lucas' mother, but perhaps she's some other family member of the boy. She's got to be a pretty distant family member as I recall the feds said that they went over every person related to Lucas with a fine tooth comb"

"When were they married?" I asked.

"There's no date. We'll have to do more checking when we get back."

"Or maybe we can just ask her ourselves?" I said.

"Yeah, right."

"Well, Paul said that she called the office and wants to talk to us after she buries her husband."

"Now that will be an interesting conversation," Gina said.

At that point, we began packing up, both of us moving in heavy silence as we contemplated what was ahead of us. I carried our luggage out to the car in two trips while Gina collected herself in the bathroom. I checked out at the front desk, exchanging the metal keys for a paid receipt. The warm, salty air hit us as we walked to our car in self-imposed silence, both of us lost in our thoughts.

❖ ❖ ❖

The trip back to Lakewood was largely uneventful. Gina and I took turns driving, switching at each fill-up of the gas tank. We each filled our own legal pads with more notes and various lists of things we needed to do. We were both anxious to work the leads, and anxious for our own personal reasons as well.

It seemed like a lifetime ago that I talked with Deana. My life felt empty and I felt more alone than ever before. My desire to hear her voice or feel the gentle touch of her hand on mine increased with every hour that passed. Gina spoke of missing her daughter, although her desire to be with her was offset by the growing problems with her live-in boyfriend.

The scenery gradually changed from a lush green to a dark brown with our northern procession and change in latitude. Much like the change from pastel colors to shades of brown and gray, so too did our moods change.

❖ ❖ ❖

I dropped Gina off at her house at 6:35 a.m., and arrived at my apartment just after 7:00, flipping on the television for the illusion of company to overcome the deep-seated loneliness I felt.

As *The Today Show* bobble heads were talking about continued troubles in the Middle East, along with questions about the Reagan White House possibly being embroiled in the Iran Contra scandal, I took a look around my apartment to make sure it was just as I left it. Amid the noise of politicians and paid analysts flapping their lips, all appeared fine.

I hurriedly unpacked my things and jumped into the shower, thinking about our next moves in the murder investigation of my uncle. While towel drying my hair, I winced in pain as I moved over the lump on the side of my head. Looking in the mirror, I saw the obvious discoloration from the bruise extending down the left side of my head. It was also the first time I noticed the pain that extended from my eye socket to my jaw. It was a fitting souvenir from our trip to 'Wally World,' I thought. Not quite like the movies, where someone can take a punch and have too little, or sometimes too much, to show for it.

I shaved and put on a freshly dry-cleaned suit, making sure that my gun was secured in my shoulder holster. I couldn't shake the spookiness I felt from our trip and the deep and dark ugliness that seemed to engulf every aspect of this case.

Despite the anonymous telephone warning we received before leaving, I returned home in an old Chevy instead of the predicted pine box. A win for me, I thought.

I arrived at the office just before 8:00. Annie was already busy at her desk. She greeted me with a warm but somewhat reserved 'hello' and announced that a fresh pot of coffee was ready. Before I could walk into my office, Annie said "Marc, we need to talk. Grab a cup of coffee. You're going to need it."

I placed my briefcase on the floor and pulled a chair next to her desk after setting my briefcase down in front of her desk.

"Ouch, Marc. Are you alright? Annie asked as she spied the bluish-purple discoloration on the side of my head."

"I'm fine, Annie. So, what's up?"

"A lot of things happened since you've been gone, Marc, and not too many of them good," she said. "You heard about Cooper."

"I did. What do we know?"

"The police and coroner have already ruled his death a suicide, but his wife doesn't believe it. She wants to meet with you as soon as possible, but doesn't want the police to know. Apparently, she found some things of his that she wants you to see."

"Seems like there's a lot of that going around, lately."

"What do you mean?"

"First Martin Tingsley, and now Sadie Cooper. Any idea of what these 'things' are?"

"She wouldn't say. She was very upset when she called late yesterday, when you were on the road. I heard her talking to Paul through my extension that I didn't hang up when I transferred the call. Paul did not even know I was listening. Whatever she found, she wants to give it to you only."

"You're going to make a great detective yet," I said with a smile. "When is his funeral?"

"It's actually today. It's going to be a private ceremony. Family and close friends only. He was already cremated. Apparently, it was his wish. His wife said she would call you after the service."

"That quick, huh? Interesting. Anything else?"

"Oh, there were a lot of other telephone messages about the case. Paul seemed to be getting upset about the time this case is taking away from the investigative business, or his security business, to be more accurate. Anyway, I took the liberty of screening most of them, and I put all of them into envelopes that I prioritized based on the quality of the caller and the specificity of the information. I think you've got a few promising leads in there, Marc. And then there's this…" Annie's tone was punctuated with a note of hesitation."

"There's what?" I asked.

I watched as Annie unlocked the desk drawer using a key she removed from her purse. She pulled out a yellow evidence bag with today's date. She removed a cassette tape from the bag and put it into a cassette player she had on her desk. "You need to hear this," Annie said as she pressed the play button that had a green, sideways triangle embossed over the black button.

It was the voice of a man who talked above labored breathing. No 'hello," no formal introductions, and no pleasantries. The man on the other end of the phone went right into the meat of the matter.

"I'll be honest with you because frankly, I've got nothing to lose. I'm dying, you see. The doctors said that I'll be dead in a few months and suggested I get my affairs in order. Just to be clear, I'm not any hero by wanting to tell you what I know. To be truthful, I'm a coward. I'm afraid… I don't want to die. But there's nothing I can do about that now. Maybe if I tell you everything I know I can score some points with my maker."

There were several seconds of virtual silence, broken by what sounded like muted beeps of hospital machines and rustling.

"I want to meet with Marc and Gina, who should be back in Lakewood by now if my sources are correct. And I'm sure they are. Yes, I have sources who know exactly what they have done, who they talked to, and what was said." The labored voice continued.

"And I hope Marc's head feels better and Gina wasn't hurt too bad from those unfortunate incidents in Miami. They don't have any idea how close they came to not coming back. Well, maybe they do.

No matter…" his gruff voice trailed off in a stupor of drugs, pain and fatigue.

"You might know who I am, but in case you don't, my name is Roger Braun. I'm in room 510 at St. Elizabeth's Hospital and expect to be here until they move me to the morgue or some other place to die. I need to see Marc and Gina today. Please. Please." His voice trailed off and there was a rustle leading up to the noise created by a telephone handset being placed on its cradle. Then silence.

"Has Paul heard this?" I asked

"No, he doesn't even know about it. I came in early this morning and the first thing I did was to check the tape. It was almost full. I listened to the last few minutes of the tape to make sure we did not miss any messages when I heard this one. I immediately took my cassette recorder and made you a copy, then I put a fresh reel on the telephone tape deck. I locked the original in the tape cabinet."

"What time do you think this came in?"

"It had to come in between 7:00 and 7:30 this morning, based on the message right before it from one of Paul's security guards who called right at seven."

Annie, do you know who this guy is?

"No, I don't Marc. Do you?"

"I think so. This is the guy that took a shotgun to his girlfriend about 30 year ago. She was a dancer at a local strip club and he supposedly caught her cheating on him with one of the club patrons. He shot both of her kneecaps off with a 12 gauge. She lived and he served his time."

"Based on what you just told me, he doesn't sound like someone who would be involved in the homosexual community," Annie said.

"Maybe not, but there were rumors about his potential involvement with a missing person case in the late 1970's, not too long after he got out of prison."

"So?"

"It was an adolescent boy. There was a big to-do about Braun and a cop being suspects in a kidnapping ring. The body of the boy was later found somewhere in a wooded area, pretty badly decomposed. A post-mortem determined that the boy had been tortured before he was murdered. I don't remember the whole story, but I do know that no one was arrested. I'll head down to the paper or the library and look through the archives. I'll call Jenkins and see if he'll meet with me to give me the inside scoop on this case. He was one of the first responding officers, but would never talk about it."

Annie looked away, pivoting with her elbow on her desk and holding her chin in her hand. I could see tears welling up in her eyes. "What a sick world this is. What sick people. How can you deal with this crap, Marc?"

Saying nothing, I stood up and put my hand on her shoulder, offering little comfort. After all, what could I say? I picked up my briefcase and entered my office, shutting the door behind me.

I turned on the classical station on the radio, letting the music set my mood for the day. My thoughts turned from the sick and ugly to the warm and beautiful, as I reached into my desk and held the card I received from Deana before my trip. I read it, along with the note from the cookies I took on our trip, and must have dozed off in my chair.

Sleep was not long as a knock on my door jarred me just after 10:00 a.m. It was Gina, who walked in carrying a fresh cup of McDonald's coffee for each of us. Despite just getting off the road, she looked quite rested and smartly dressed. She sat in the chair in front of my desk and smiled as she saw what I was holding in my lap.

"Good morning Romeo! Annie brought me up to speed. I heard the tape. So, when are we going to see Braun?"

"We better do it today," I said. We've also got to talk with Martin and his wife, and whenever she's ready, Cooper's widow." I placed the card and note from Deana back into my desk drawer.

"So, have you called Deana yet, letting her know that you're back?" Gina asked.

"Not yet. I've been putting it off, thinking maybe absence doesn't really make the heart grow fonder. Even worse, I'm worried about her. I mean, I'm worried about her being seen with me, bringing her into whatever world we've stumbled into, Gina. It seems like we're rubbing elbows with some seriously sick people. And they seem to know our every move."

I know, Marc. Bob gave me an ultimatum this morning. Either I quit my job and this case in particular, or he is going to move out,"

Gina said.

"And?"

"Well, I'm here, aren't I?"

❖ ❖ ❖

"Welcome back you two, we need to talk. My office. Ten minutes." Paul bellowed his not-so-warm welcome, appearing agitated and hurried. Gina and I looked at each other quizzically, trying to make sense of Paul's unexpected abrasiveness as he pulled the door to my office shut.

After gathering our investigative notes from our trip, fresh legal pads and coffee refills, Gina and I filed in to Paul's office like obedient schoolchildren summoned by a school principal. Paul immediately noticed the bruise on the side of my head. "Looks like you should have ducked," he said without expression.

"What in the hell is your problem, Paul?" Gina asked acerbically and in a tone I've seldom heard her use.

Ignoring Gina, Paul wanted the cliff notes version of our findings in Florida. We explained the events as they happened, noting that the only common thread seems to be young boys, possible blackmail, and a homosexual mafia, none of which seemed to have anything to do with my uncle's murder.

The debriefing was unlike the deliberate formality and organized case review initially conducted. Paul seemed to merely want the case over.

"What's going on, Paul? Why does it seem you've lost interest in this case? Why the attitude?" I asked. Gina and I waited for an answer, which was several long seconds in coming.

"The district attorney's office contacted me while you were gone. They are conducting a review of our license. It's the first license review of a private investigator's agency in the last 75 years in the state, and these usually don't end well," Paul said flatly.

"On what basis?" Gina asked.

"I don't know. They don't have to tell us. It's their right of oversight. But I will tell you that it's because of this case," Paul said.

Paul explained that his contact within the Lakewood Police Department works out with one of the investigators in the D.A.'s office. According to Paul's source, the district attorney is complaining that we are interfering with their investigation, and they are also getting heat from the feds. Also, we are making some prominent people nervous. These people want to see our investigation shut down, and they feel that only way they could shut down our investigation, is to shut us down.

"Shutting down the agency wouldn't stop me, Paul. They'd have to kill me before I quit, now," I said.

"Yeah, and they almost did, Marc. And that was over a thousand miles away from here. What do you think they'll do to you here? And I've got too much riding on my business, and starting the security business, to have the state shut me down. I'll lose everything."

Just as I was about to tell Paul how little I cared, Gina suddenly piped up. "Stall them. Tell them we've hit a brick wall and we're backing off. In the meantime, me and Marc will follow up on the leads we have. Call Mary from the paper. Tell her our trip was a bust. Tell everyone you can think of that we're done. Give us a week, Paul."

Paul sat back in his chair, contemplating what Gina was proposing. "Three days. I'll give you three days. Make the most of it."

"You expect us to solve this case in three days, especially now that things are happening? Really?" I said to Paul.

"Yes, *especially* because things are happening. The wrong things. I've got to go to Columbus tonight and will be gone for three days. When I get back, we're done with this case. I'll hold off the rabid dogs until then."

❖ ❖ ❖

I shut the door to my office and called Deana, letting her know I was back from my trip. "I missed you," she said. "I kept waiting for your call. I was beginning to think you didn't like my cookies," she said, trying to keep it light. "Can I see you today?"

"I planned on it. I've got an extra half-hour for lunch. I thought we could go to the marina, maybe just talk."

"Anything wrong?" I asked.

"No, of course not. I just want to see you away from other people."

"Okay. How does 11:30 sound?"

"Like a plan," she said. After saying our warm goodbyes, I hung up the phone and felt a surge of energy course through me. I asked Gina to set something up with the Tingsleys. She used my office phone and spoke to Mary. An appointment was scheduled for 7:00 p.m. today at their home.

CHAPTER 20

The Extreme Unction of Roger Braun

We then drove to St. Elizabeth's Hospital to meet Roger Braun. Just as we were about to enter room 510, a nurse walked out. "Can I help you?"

"We're here to see Roger Braun. He called this morning and wanted some company," I replied.

"Are you two cops? Asked the nurse.

"Why?"

"Well, he never got much company for as long as he's been in this ward, which is longer than most. Now, all of a sudden, he's getting visits from detectives and G-men," she said bluntly. "Go on in. I'll be coming back to give him a shot for pain in a little while. You can stay until then."

I walked into the room first, followed closely by Gina. In front of me was a ghost of a man lying in bed, the headboard raised up about a third of the way to a fully seated position. He had IVs and other tubes pushing stuff in, and others pulling stuff out.

Roger Braun turned his head to watch us walk in, then turned back forward. "Well if it isn't Marc, and you must be Gina," he said with some labor. "Sit, sit," he instructed, raising his arm level with the bed, the skin of his arm hanging down like a heavy, wet towel.

After the exchanging of some forced pleasantries, we asked Roger to tell us everything he knew about the murder of my uncle, and whatever else he knew about whatever it was in which we found ourselves involved.

"You two sure know how to stir up a hornet's nest, I'll give you that," Roger said in a tone stronger than expected.

"Well then Roger, why don't you tell us about those hornets, and why they're all riled up. Enlighten us. And while you're at it, rumor has it that you've been keeping company with cops and federal agents over the last few days. Why don't you fill us in on that, too," I said.

"Well, it looks like we both have our sources, Marc," he said, unaware that my source was merely the nurse we met on our way in. And so, he began talking.

He described how he shot his girlfriend in the early 1950's, and how he managed to game the legal system after his release from prison. He spoke of his sexual encounters with both women and men, the latter stemming from his experiences in prison. He admitted to several rapes of both boys and girls, young and old, and explained how he got away with all of them. He said that he is a member of a secret organization that involved very powerful and high profile people in Lakewood and at higher levels of all organizations.

"Somehow, Marc, you managed to strike at the center of this group of powerful men. You are making a lot of people nervous, and your life is about to become worthless if you don't stop asking questions. These people would rather kill you than look at you."

I scoffed, stopping him nearly midstream. "Yeah, well just who are these 'bogeymen' of which you speak," I asked as sarcastically as I could manage.

"Sonny, you've got a lot to learn, and I'd lose that attitude of yours if I was you. You can choose to believe me, I don't care. Your cockiness is unbecoming of you. In fact, it could be the death of you," he said without emotion.

Gina stepped in, gently pushing me back and taking over the conversation. "Tell us, Roger, tell us what you know. I understand and I know about these people. Marc is just getting his first taste of this. I was a cop once, you know. And I've seen things. So, go on. Give us names, specifics, please."

Looking at me but talking to Gina, Roger said that my uncle discovered a child sex ring operating in Lakewood. Child prostitutes, taken from their homes at an early age, and passed around to rich and powerful men, some who are community leaders. Some in government. Some in the church. He said that none of this is new, but has its roots back to government operations decades ago.

"Oh come on, Gina, this guy's a flippin' kook. He's probably on morphine or some hallucinogenic, and he's yanking our chains," I protested.

"Marc, be quiet for once and listen," Gina shot back.

"Marc, put down your pride for a minute and understand one thing. What you don't know can and most likely will kill you. It does not matter whether you believe me or not. Your belief, or lack of it, makes no difference, not to me, and certainly not to these people, not to anyone, except that it shows just how ignorant you truly are. Keep believing what you want to believe. Keep thinking that everything you see is exactly what it appears to be."

Turning his gaze to Gina, Roger said "I guess he's not ready to hear about experimental mind control and Nazi experiments. I guess I'll leave that to you to tell him about."

I think it was Gina's lack of surprise or reaction that struck me the most. And then there was something in Roger's voice, his tone and delivery hit me like a ton of bricks.

I felt stunned, but did not know why. At that moment, I felt like I knew nothing at all. It must have shown on my face, as Roger looked at me and said, "Good, I see that I'm making some progress, anyway." Roger took a tissue and spit a wad of thick phlegm into it, turning the outside into a reddish brown stain. He continued to talk.

"Your uncle Gerry lived in his own personal hell, but it was one of his own making. He was cocky like you, Marc, except that he was cocky about his lifestyle, thinking that he could hide his homosexuality and laugh at how stupid your family was. He had the cover of many other high-profile homosexuals in the community, including the president judge of the county, the former district attorney, and others of power." Roger struggled a bit as he continued to talk, seemingly enjoying having an audience.

"I don't know who killed your uncle, but I can tell you that he was way out of control. He was drinking too much, and his booze muscles led him to get brave with his random hook-ups and with prominent people as well. Somehow, he got his hands on some pictures that showed the former president county judge, the deputy sheriff, and the editor of the newspaper in compromising positions with young boys. He got his hands on others pictures of ceremonies, including one where a young boy was murdered in a ceremony to the devil. He was even blackmailing a businessman and a priest."

"C'mon, Gina, this is bull. You can't possibly believe this, can you?"

"Gina, I'm getting tired. Do me a favor. Hand me my shoes from the bottom of my closet."

"And just where do you think you're going? You're all hooked up?" I said to Roger.

Gina shot me a disapproving glance as she got up from her chair and did as she was told. She lifted the shoes from the closet and carefully handed them to him. Neither appeared to be worn. He took his left shoe from her hands, lifted up the insole and pulled out three Polaroid pictures from a makeshift hiding place.

"Here, maybe these will convince you, Sherlock," Roger said, handing me the photographs.

As I looked at the pictures, I could feel whatever contents were in my stomach gradually making their way to the back of my throat. I was looking at the most hideous and evil scene captured in still images.

"These are a joke, right? A Halloween party or a prank?"

"No Marc. This is a world inside of ours that no one believes exists. This is the world that people will mock, like you have, as fantasy. Here are your respected leaders, in all of their evil glory."

Roger started to cough strenuously now, and his breathing became much more labored. He motioned for Gina to come closer to his side.

"I did a lot of bad things in my life. I am truly sorry for everything I did, everyone I hurt, and killed. I don't want to go to hell." Tears began streaming down his face, puddling on the sanitary white pillowcase under his head.

Gina inched closer to him and picked up his frail hand. What she said next surprised me.

"Roger, do you know Jesus?"

Roger looked at Gina with a look of surprise, nearly mirroring my own surprise.

"I know the devil. But Jesus? I don't know. What does Jesus have to do with anything?"

Gina explained to Roger that the way to avoid hell is to profess Jesus as his Lord and Savior. She spent a few minutes explaining that Jesus died for our sins, and we could be forgiven if we profess our belief and submit ourselves to Him. She had Roger say the sinner's prayer with her, and left a small New Testament in his hand.

By the time Roger ended the prayer and his last tear fell upon his pillow, he was spent. I could feel a cloud lift from the room, thinking, perhaps that Roger had met his end. He continued to breathe, although he was obviously straining. Just then a nurse came into the room with a vial and syringe and told us it was time to leave.

Gina bent over and kissed his forehead, lingering long enough over him to say a short prayer. The nurse gave her the time and room, nodding to both of us as we left.

We walked to the elevators in silence. I could see tears welling in Gina's eyes, but could not think of anything to say. We entered the elevator and left the building before either of us spoke.

"What you did back there, Gina. The talk of Jesus. Do your really think there's a chance for a guy like that?"

"Marc, Jesus died for all of us. You tell me that I've got to see the big picture of things. You've got to see the even bigger picture," she said.

❖ ❖ ❖

It was 10:40 a.m. when we got to our vehicle in the hospital parking lot. Gina broke the silence and asked to see the photographs while I drove back to the office. Like a protective brother, I hesitated as I was trying to come to grips with the horror that they depicted. I handed them to her with the warning that they are worse than anything I've ever seen.

Gina studied each picture in silence. If she was shocked or horrified, it was difficult to tell.

The first picture showed a boy who appeared to be 8 to10 years old, fully naked, performing oral sex on an older man wearing nothing more than a devil's mask. I counted four other older males standing in a semi-circle around the pair, each holding a lit candle. Hot wax from the candles held by each of the men clearly dripped onto the boy's bare back. The boy had his eyes fixed at the camera. He had a look of pain and fear, while the men sported smiles and grins behind their own individual hideously evil looking masks.

The second picture showed the same young boy, bent forward over a chair, being violated by another man while the others stood in observance. The image on the boy's face was a horrific combination of pain and fear. The boy's blood was clearly evident running down his leg, a result of the intimate violation. This time, a pentagram was partially visible on the boy's back, appearing to have been crudely carved by a sharp instrument. A towel soaked in blood laid at the boy's feet.

The third picture was, by far, the most horrifying. The boy shown in the previous images now appeared to be laying, face up, on a raised cot like structure. Six men in total, each one naked and wearing either full or partial masks covering their faces, surrounded the lifeless body of the young boy. Although not completely visible, it was evident that the boy's genitals had been severed and he was at least partially opened up near the bottom of his breastbone. All six men were holding leaded crystal glasses containing what appeared like blood, presumably from the boy. Like some morbid lipstick, blood stained the lips of the men and the rims of the glasses.

As I pulled into the office parking lot, Gina said that she would be in my office when I got back from lunch with Deana. She wished me a good lunch, and like a loving sister, told me to make the most out of my time with Deana. "The case will be here when you get back, and so will I," Gina said. Just then, she exited my car and walked into our office building.

I sat for a minute, contemplating the insidious evil of what I had just seen and the enormity of what I have yet to see. I felt more frightened than I ever felt in my life. I struggled to remember the words to the prayer Gina said with Roger.

I pulled up to the rear doors of Deana's office building at 11:35, uncharacteristically late for our lunch date. She was already standing outside of the door, waiting for me to arrive. I stepped out and opened the passenger door for her, closing it gently behind her. I got in and immediately hugged Deana, taking her by surprise. "My God, it's so good to see you," I said. "And I do mean that I thank God for you," I added.

"Marc, what's wrong? You're shaking. What happened to your head? Are you alright? Deana's questions were coming at a rapid pace, each filled with more concern than the last. "Let me see your head," she said as she gently moved my head toward her with her soft hand. "Have you seen a doctor?"

I didn't reply. I could feel myself trembling and without warning, tears began to flood down my face. I was embarrassed. Real men don't cry for no reason, or without good reason. The only acceptable reasons I could think of was the death of a man's mother or his dog, and neither fit this situation.

"What's going on Marc? Please tell me. I'm here for you. I want to help you. I… I love you. I really love you."

"I love you too, Deana," I said, doing my best to hide my tears from her. "I…I'm sorry. Please don't look at me. I don't want you to see me like this. It's just a weak moment, that's all." After gaining some of my composure back, I joked that her radiant beauty was too much for my mere mortal eyes to handle.

And there it was, in the back of a cold office building, on a gray and overcast day and in the wake of one of the most demonic things that I've seen that I professed my love for the woman of my dreams. And it was at one of the weakest times in my life.

We drove right to the marina, where we spent the next hour overlooking the bay and watching men readying their boats for the season. Deana packed a small basket of fruit and other goodies, which we ate as we talked about the possibility of making a life together.

"I'm not sure I'm your best investment, Deana," I said, thinking about my career and all of my recent experiences.

"I'll be the judge of that, Marc. I've got good instincts."

❖ ❖ ❖

Gina and I left the office to make it to Martin and Mary Tingsley's house by 7:00. Their house was located just off a busy road in a lower middle class section of Lakewood. The front porch light was on, apparently in anticipation of our arrival. The door was opened by Mary before we even reached the porch.

"Come in," Mary said to both of us. "Martin is in the living room. Can I get either of you something to drink? We have coffee, soft drinks and even some juice boxes, if that's more to your liking," Mary said with a chuckle.

"I'll have something cold," I said to Mary. "Me too," added Gina.

"Where's your mom and the kids?" Gina prodded.

"They went to a movie and should be gone until 8:30 or so," said Mary.

As we were seated in the living room, we could sense that Martin was a lot more relaxed than our first meeting. After exchanging small talk about our trip that was more about routes and driving conditions than our findings, we asked what Martin had withheld from us.

"I just needed to know that I could trust you, I guess. And I also needed to know that you would make it back from Florida alive. Seriously," he added.

"Well, you can, we did and we're here. So Martin, what did you not tell us?" I asked.

"I suppose you heard about a guy named Cooper— the late Benjamin Cooper?" He asked.

"Yes, of course. He supposedly killed himself. Why? How do you know him?"

"Well, I was with him and your uncle on the night your uncle was murdered. In fact, we had breakfast together at the diner that morning. Just me and Jerry for breakfast, I mean. I saw Cooper later at your, uh, I mean your uncle's house."

With his admissions, I could feel anger building up inside of me. Why didn't he tell us this when we first met, I wondered. As usual, Gina could read me and quickly jumped in, softly asking the same questions I was about ready to ask in a not-so-gentle manner.

"Did you tell the police all of this?" Gina asked, looking at both for signs of deception.

"Of course, we told them everything, well almost everything," Martin said. The only thing I didn't tell them was that I saw your uncle right after everybody went home from the party. I don't remember exactly what time it was, but Cooper was at the house at that time. I wanted to talk to Jerry more about my mother's murder, which was the reason I asked to meet him for breakfast that morning. He knew I was on a mission and was not about to give up, so at breakfast he told me to stop over later that evening, after his family left, and he would show me some things that might help fill in the blanks about my mom's accident."

"Go on," I prompted.

"When I got to the house, though, I felt like I was interrupting something. Not sexual, but like a business meeting. It was weird. Jerry acted like I was an imposition in front of Cooper. I could tell he did not want me there. So I asked him if I could use the bathroom before I left. I went into the bathroom and turned the water on. I slipped out and walked into Jerry's bedroom and opened the top drawer of his dresser where I knew he kept some photographs.

I knew I didn't have much time, and I also knew I couldn't take everything there as he would know it was me, so I flipped through the pictures and took a few that I thought were the most important to prove the existence of a sadistic, satanic sex ring. The same sex ring and people who were responsible for hurting me and killing my mother."

"That's a pretty gutsy move, Martin, especially since you know that he would eventually find out. That is, of course, unless you knew that he was going to be killed. Seems like a rather lucky break for you, doesn't it?" I said with an accusatory tone.

"Marc," Gina interrupted. "Go on Martin."

"I slipped back into the bathroom, flushed the toilet and turned off the water. I stuffed the pictures in my pants and left. Jerry and Cooper were still sitting at the dining room table when I walked out the front door. Jerry was alive when I last saw him."

"Did you tell the police about the pictures, Martin?" Gina asked.

"No, I was not about to admit that I stole them, or that I was there just hours before Jerry was killed. They already refused to investigate what happened to me, the murder of my mom, so what's the point? Plus, some of the people in the photographs are connected to the police."

Gina turned to Mary, who was seated next to Martin with her arm interlocked with his. Picking up on something I wasn't, Gina asked Mary if she would show us the photographs.

"That was five years ago," Mary protested. What makes you think we still have them after such a long time?"

"Please, Mary, let us see the pictures," insisted Gina.

Mary let out a sigh and stood up, touching Martin on his shoulder. "I'll be right back, honey. It'll be alright." She disappeared up a flight of stairs and could be heard unlocking and opening a metal box. She returned downstairs with an envelope and handed it to Gina.

I moved behind Gina as she opened the envelope, revealing five pictures similar in appearance to those given to us by Roger Braun earlier in the day. Upon the mere sight of the photos, Martin began to tremble. He also began exhibiting an unusual tic, a jerky, involuntary movement that involved the right side of his face and eye. Mary disappeared momentarily into the kitchen, returning with a glass of water and a pill she handed to Martin. He swallowed the pill and water without objection.

The five photographs depicted images of two different young boys and at least six different older men.

One picture was different than the rest. It clearly showed six older men, dressed in what appeared to be matching black hooded bathrobes, seated on a wooden bench that best resembled a church pew. An upside down cross was carved into the wood of the bench, with the six men divided evenly on either side of the carving. Their smiling faces were uncovered. Behind the men was an altar of sorts that appeared to be made of wood and ivory.

A closer inspection of the altar suggested that the ivory was not ivory at all, but was crudely fashioned of small bones. A black curtain was draped over the center of the altar, showing the majority of an elaborate star-like image in a circle in red. It matched the necklaces of those we saw in Florida, and Cooper's necklace Gina saw. Other symbols appeared in the background of this particular photograph, although they were not clear without magnification.

We readily recognized three of the six men. One was our gun-toting Florida 'friend' Porter Landers. Another was Benjamin Cooper, the late businessman, and a third was an investigator with the district attorney's office.

We looked at the other four photos, repulsed at what we saw. Two pictures showed the same group of men sodomizing a very young boy with an ornate brass-like staff. Fresh and dried blood, indicated by different colors, was visible on the rod and child, and on the hands of two of the men.

The other photograph was beyond comprehension. It showed a dinner table with a silver platter in the center, On the platter appeared to be an unclothed infant doll, the kind that a small girl would carry around. This doll, however, if that's indeed what it was, appeared to have been caught in a fire as it was significantly discolored. Even if it was a joke or a prank, it was certainly a bad one. The tablecloth was ornately decorated with symbols and what appeared to be ancient writing. Candles were lit on both sides of the platter, and dishes were spread out to match each seat at the table.

"This is the stuff nightmares are made of," I murmured to Gina.

Gina gathered the pictures together and looked up at Mary, who was holding Martin's head against her chest.

"You can keep those. We have copies that are in a safe deposit box and another set elsewhere," Mary said, anticipating our question.

"Thanks, Mary. Martin, were you at any of these places, those in the photos? Gina asked.

"Yes," Martin said weakly.

"Were these taken in Lakewood?"

"Yes."

"Do you know where? At some point, could you take us to where these were taken?"

"No. I mean, I was there, but I was drugged and they put a pillowcase over my head, or made me do things as they drove me to these places."

"Do you know of anyone else who was there, who might be able to show us where these places are?"

"You mean like other kids?"

"Yeah."

"Not anymore."

"What do you mean?"

'They're all dead, or missing."

"Does the name Luca Manning mean anything to you, Martin?" Gina asked.

"Yes, why?"

"Do you know him?"

"I did."

"Where is he"

Martin began weeping, softly at first, then inconsolably. "They made us do it. They made us kill him."

A chill ran up my spine. Gina began tearing up, and Mary held Martin's head, rocking him back and forth like an infant. After a lengthy silence, I asked Martin if anyone else knew he had these pictures.

"No. My mother had copies of each of these original photos, along with a few other originals with her in her car when she was pushed over the bluff. Whoever killed her took them, not knowing there were copies. After she was killed, somebody tore up her house looking for these. You better be careful with them."

"Martin, I'm going to ask you one last time. How did my uncle fit into all of this? Was he any of the men who hurt you? Was he a member of whatever sick club this was, or is? I want the truth from you, because I'm going to find out anyway. One way or another."

"No, he was not part of the brotherhood, as they called it, but many of his friends were. At breakfast that morning, he told me that Houghton, Landers and others from Florida were, and in a big way. I came to him for protection. He knew how bad these people are. Marc, he told me that he loved me, and promised to keep me safe."

"How did he plan to do that?"

"He wanted me to meet him that night. I think he was going to give me the evidence I needed to take to someone. Maybe these pictures were part of that evidence, but he never had the chance."

"Do you think Cooper was there to stop him?"

"No. I don't know."

"Martin, were you and my uncle intimate?"

"I loved him, and he loved me."

"One more question, Martin, and I want the truth. How much of this does my father know? My family?"

"Marc, at least on this, I can promise you that your father was totally clueless. Your entire family was. Well, maybe with one exception. Your cousin the priest. He knows much more, but was held by the vow of silence. Yet, there was one thing Jerry was most afraid of."

"What, exactly?"

"That your father would find out. He said it would kill him. Your dad was proud of his brother."

"Mary, is there anything else we should know? If so, now is the time to tell us," Gina gently quizzed Mary,

Mary had a thousand yard stare as she held Martin. Several long seconds of silence were broken when she said "This is bigger than you can imagine. No one who knows what we know is safe from these demons. And that's what they are, demons, straight from the pit of hell."

Just then, Martin broke free of Mary's grasp and sat up, seemingly looking though us. Out of nowhere, he said, "Just follow the yellow brick road." He then closed his eyes and laid his head back in Mary's arms.

We both looked at Mary, who whispered that he has been saying that a lot, especially since receiving news of our investigation. From her arms, he whispered "The yellow brick road, it's stained by blood." He fell asleep quickly, presumably from the medication he was given by Mary.

We left the Tingsley's house before Mary's mother and the children returned, and drove straight back to the office, constantly checking to see if we were being followed. We were relieved that we didn't see anyone.

❖ ❖ ❖

We had put in a full day and were mentally and physically exhausted by the time Gina and I returned to the office. I put on a fresh pot of coffee while Gina called home to check on her daughter, who was in the loving care of her mother, who all but moved in since her troubles with Bob. I heard Gina ask her mother to keep her safe, undoubtedly in response to the morbid aspects of the day.

I filled a mug with coffee and was already in my office for a few minutes before Gina entered. I made several copies of each photograph and stored the originals in the safe in Paul's office, at least for now. I didn't have the time since we had been back to update the index cards on my board, and mused how quickly the landscape of white cards and colored yarn had changed in such a short time.

Gina pulled up her chair to my desk and we both sat in stunned silence staring at the photographs spread over my desk, drinking coffee and smoking our share of cigarettes.

"So, what do you think the chances are of us coincidentally getting photographs like these from two different people on the same day?" I asked Gina.

"As strange as it seems, I guess I can see it. Good timing, I suppose. Divine assistance, more accurately. We're just back from our trip and Tingsley has a change of heart. Braun knows he's not long for this world," Gina said.

"So what are these, some new type of trading card for the rich and perverted?" I asked "Who takes photographs like this? Who keeps pictures like this? What do they do with them? Are they trophies or sick mementos for the scrapbooks of the damned?"

"Marc, I'm thinking that someone has got to be looking for these, at least the pictures that Braun gave us. And it won't be any secret that we paid him a visit today."

"Well, based on the people we've identified in the photographs, just who do we take them to? We need to identify everybody in the photographs, at least as best we can, including the victims. We know more than half of them, so the rest shouldn't be that difficult. It's got to be a close circle of friends. We need to get exposure to this to take the heat off us, too," I said.

"We can make this a priority for tomorrow. I'll call Cooper's widow and see when we can meet with her. Maybe she can shed some more light on things," Gina added.

It was 10:30 when we left the office, going our separate ways. I asked Gina to call me at my apartment as soon as she got home. I considered stopping at the Towne Bar for a drink, but decided against it, choosing mental clarity over the chemical blurring of unpleasant memories.

I walked in to my apartment and did a thorough walk through to make certain nothing was amiss. As all appeared fine, I set my briefcase on the kitchen table and turned on the television.

CHAPTER 21

Wednesday, May 28, 1987

Annie was already at her desk when I arrived at the office at 7:30 a.m. She began asking questions about the murder investigation as soon as I walked in, wanting to know how our meetings went yesterday and if we were any closer to solving my uncle's murder. Frankly, I didn't know what to tell her as I could not determine if we were any closer to closing this case or if we had fallen into a perverse version of the Wizard of Oz. I suspected we were much closer to the latter than the former, but kept my musings to myself.

With Paul gone, the office was quiet. He was operating his security operation from the road, making assignments from some motel room in Columbus. Meanwhile, we were counting down the hours we had before Paul pulled the plug on us. Gina felt resentment, and so did I, about this self-imposed deadline stemming from governmental intimidation, especially considering everything we've been uncovering.

As I re-entered the front office to look over the mail and get some coffee, Annie asked me how things were going with Deana. I was suddenly thrust from thinking about the perverse and profane to the beauty of a woman I didn't deserve. It was a mental U-turn that I found difficult to maneuver.

"It's going fine, Annie," I said, not wanting to give her any specifics from my encounter the previous day. "Whoa, go easy on the details, Romeo," she said, smiling while she filed folders into a metal cabinet. I was uncharacteristically short with her compared to the previous weeks.

"I'm sorry, Marc, I didn't mean to pry. I just haven't seen you much, and I miss thinking about the prospect of a budding new romance," she said. "Anyway, I don't mean to be blunt, but you look terrible, and not in the hungover way, either. Maybe I should keep my questions to the case instead."

"Do yourself a favor and don't ask about either, okay Annie?" I walked back in to my office and shut the door. I felt bad about the way I treated her, but I could not shake the darkness I felt in the depth of my soul.

Just after eight, Gina knocked and opened the door to my office, walking in and closing the door behind her.

"What's going on, Marc? Annie said that you bit her head off this morning."

"What do you mean asking me that? You know what's going on. We're dealing in some pretty strange stuff. And we're not getting any closer on who murdered my uncle." I apologized to Gina, then stuck my head out and apologized to Annie.

"Now that's more like the Marc I know. Let's go over what we know for the next hour or so, and then I'll call Mrs. Cooper to see if we can get any useful information out of her.

Just then, Annie knocked on my office door, opening it just enough for her to stick her head inside. "I heard what you just said, Gina, and I want to tell you that you won't have to make that call."

"Why not?"

"Mrs. Cooper is here. She's sitting in the front office, waiting to talk to both of you."

Gina and I looked blankly at each other. Breaking the brief silence, I joked to Gina that we've got people beating down our doors to talk to us. "How's that for a change?" I mused.

"Okay, send her in," Gina instructed Annie.

Sadie Cooper, a slender 50 year-old woman doing her best to look 30, bleached-blond, red fingernail polish and attired in a low-cut black dress that seemed more appropriate for a cocktail party than an early morning meeting with a private detective, brushed by Annie to make her way into the office. She immediately sat down in the chair in front of my desk. She was carrying a large purse that could have doubled for an overnight bag in my world.

"Mrs. Cooper, please, help yourself to a seat," I said with suitable sarcasm that had not gone unnoticed by Gina.

"Thank you Mr. Stiles."

"We're very sorry for your loss, Mrs. Cooper," Gina said with more compassion than I could have mustered at this point after finding herself without a chair.

"About that. My husband did not kill himself. He did not even own a gun. I can assure you that he was murdered."

"Seems like a lot of that going around these days." I heard myself say that out loud, surprising even myself as well as Gina, who gave me one of those looks that could kill. "Do you know who killed him?" I asked.

Mrs. Cooper ignored my question.

Gina pulled up a chair, deliberately positioning it between me and our visitor to act as a public relations buffer. I was hardly in the mood for friendly conversation, and I had no idea why. To show that I meant business, I stood up, took off my suit coat and hung it on the back of my chair, revealing my shoulder holster and gun.

"We were just about to call you, based on you telephoning our office. We're glad you're here as we'd like to ask you some questions. But first, is there something you would like to tell us?" Gina asked.

"Yes. I want to give you the bigger picture. I doubt you will believe me, and I would not blame you if you don't. I hardly believe what I'm going to tell you, and I lived it."

Oh great. More yellow brick road, follow the bloody footprints, mind-bending, perverse crap. This time, I merely thought those words instead of saying them out loud.

"With regard to the murder of your uncle, Mr. Stiles, you will see the proof of who killed him shortly. That I promise you. You have my word, again, my promise. But you must first understand the bigger picture, or at least make an attempt to understand it. Are you willing to do that, Mr. Stiles? Ms. Russell?"

Given her promise of concluding the murder case, Gina and I both answered in the affirmative.

Sadie Cooper began to relate how she had a loveless marriage to a man who was unable to be intimate with her. She admitted that she married him partially for the money and security, as her husband was one of Lakewood's wealthiest and most respected people in the community. But he was not who he appeared to be. In fact, we would soon learn, that nothing was what it appeared to be.

For starters, she said that Benjamin Cooper was not his birth name. He was born Rudolph Fleischer in pre-war Germany. Growing up, he became a member of the Hitler Youth Party and then a full-fledged Nazi, however emigrated to the United States when he was 22 years old. After arriving in the U.S., Cooper, or Fleischer, worked at a lab for the government. Mrs. Cooper said that she did not know what his job was, and he would never talk about it.

"How did he get his start in the steel industry?" I asked.

"Government money," she said. "I don't know the particulars, but it was all set up for him by the government. Like clockwork every year or so, he would leave for a few weeks for a trip to DC or Virginia. He was very coy about telling me what he was doing."

"Mrs. Cooper, I don't mean to be short or disrespectful, but what does any of this have to do with our murder investigation?" I asked.

"There are many pieces to this puzzle and a lot of moving parts. Your uncle wandered into something he knew nothing about. It was his carnal lust, however, that ensnared him. It was his lifestyle. A lifestyle that has a very real overlap into the profane. The perverse. There is a world that exists that few know about. It is a dark underworld. It involves the demonic. Child sacrifice. Kidnapping and trafficking. Satan worship, and murder."

"Are you saying that my uncle was involved in Satanism? Child sacrifice?" I asked, becoming more agitated with each passing second.

"No, Mr. Stiles, that's not what I'm saying. But those he encountered are. It's the risk one takes when one adopts a certain lifestyle. All I ask of you is to open your mind to a world you don't know exists, and one that I'm certain you will find difficult to understand. Don't dismiss or mock what you don't understand. It does not make it any less real."

"Okay, I'll bite. Go on."

"As a matter of fact, I intend to prove what I am about to tell you." Mrs. Cooper looked at her watch.

"In just about 45 minutes from right now, I want you both to look out your window. You'll witness the arrest of the man who killed your uncle. On this, you'll readily see the proof and know that what I am telling you is the truth. As for the rest, you must work to search out the deeds of darkness, on your own, if that is what you choose to do. Or, if that is what you've been called to do, perhaps."

Gina and I looked at each other, incredulous. Not quite knowing exactly what to say, Gina asked our mysterious visitor whether she would like something to drink.

"I would love a cup of hot tea, if you have any."

"I think that could be arranged." Gina walked to the door and leaned out to Annie, asking her to run to the diner for three cups of tea and lemon. "It will just be a few minutes, Mrs. Cooper. In the meantime, why don't we get started with you telling us what we need to know." Gina grabbed two legal pads, handing me one while keeping the other for herself. As soon as Gina picked up a pen, Mrs. Cooper began talking.

"Have you ever heard of a program called MK Ultra? Project Monarch? These are secret government projects," Mrs. Cooper began.

"Yes," Gina said before I could say no.

Sadie Cooper directed her attention to me. "You will, if you decide to continue your investigation into the larger issues we face. But that will be up to you. And if you do, you might even want to take a trip to the Library of Congress and search the archives for information about those programs. It will give you a basic understanding about some important government spy operations that stem from Nazi experiments."

"The CIA? Nazi experiments? This is Lakewood, Mrs. Cooper, and not some Hollywood movie."

"Geography is irrelevant, and as to your Hollywood reference, you're closer to the truth than you might imagine. Are you a movie buff, Mr. Stiles?"

"A movie buff? No, not really."

"Well, allow me to recommend a couple of movies from the past for your future homework. I think you'll find that life does not imitate art, but art does, in fact imitate life. For starters, I would urge you to watch *Rosemary's Baby* and *The Manchurian Candidate*, but I digress. May I be allowed to continue?"

"Please," Gina piped in.

"I know that you are under a lot of pressure to stop your investigation."

"And just how do you know that," I asked.

"How do I know that in less than 45 minutes now, the murderer of your uncle will be arrested?

"I believe that remains to be seen, Mrs. Cooper. But go on."

"As I was saying. Why do you think you are being pressured to stop your investigation? Have you considered that what you've stumbled upon is much bigger than the death of your uncle, as tragic as it was? Have you asked yourselves why the police have had, in their possession, sufficient evidence to find out who killed your uncle but no one has been arrested in five years?"

"Well, yes, of course we have."

"No you really haven't. You just think you have. You are playing like you are in the little leagues, but you're in the big leagues now, whether you know it or not. You must think bigger, think outside the box."

Mrs. Cooper reached into her bag and removed a large manila envelope. She pulled out several 8x10 inch black and white prints, carefully spreading them evenly across the top of my desk, each one facing me. Gina stood up and positioned herself beside me so she could see the photos right side up.

Oh great. More photographs, I thought. As it turned out, though, these were not the type to which we've come to expect.

The first photo was of me and Gina seated at the Towne Bar, looking out of the window into the parking lot. The second picture showed me seated inside my car with Deana as a passenger, taken at least two weeks ago. The third picture was of Martin and Mary Tingsley entering our office for our initial meeting. Other pictures, each of superb quality, were of similar content. Surveillance photographs of us and our activities over the last few weeks.

Few things in life have the mental effect on a person than seeing themselves as the subject of surveillance in still life. Especially when that person performs surveillance for a living. The implications are ominous, and the effect is destabilizing.

"Okay, you have our full attention, now, Mrs. Cooper," Gina said.

"You can keep those," she said. "You can keep these too," she said as she pulled out another manila envelope containing photographs of me and Gina in Florida.

"I want to know what in the hell is going on here. I want answers, and I want them now," I said, standing up and leaning forward, purposely invading Mrs. Cooper's personal space.

"Please, Mr. Stiles, sit down. I'm not your enemy, or I wouldn't be here. In fact, I'm the reason you are both still alive. You can thank me later," she said with a wry smile.

Just then Annie walked in carrying a cardboard tray with three cups of tea, a small container of sliced lemons, and packets of honey from the diner. She placed the tray on my desk next to the photo array, which caught her attention. She stared at the photos and looked at me with a level of fright I had not seen her exhibit before. She hurriedly exited my office and shut the door behind her.

"I'm sure she'll be alright," Mrs. Cooper said, referring to Annie and her reaction to seeing the surveillance photographs.

"Let's continue, shall we? I'll try to be as precise as possible. I want to see justice to be served, in the case of your uncle and hopefully, in every case associated with this nightmare."

"Why? What's in it for you? You did not even know my uncle, did you? So what are you getting out of this"

"No, I did not know your uncle. But to answer your first question, as hard as you might find it to believe, Mr. Stiles, I'm getting back my soul. My freedom. The reclaiming of my soul, and a new life far away from here."

Mrs. Cooper reached into her bag again and held up a plane ticket.

"Where are you off to?" Gina inquired.

"Parts unknown, Ms. Russell. At 4:00 p.m. today, Lakewood and my life as the wife of Benjamin Cooper will be nothing more than a bad dream."

Something about her 'reclaiming her soul' resonated deep with my spirit. She certainly had my attention, and Gina's as well. We watched as she removed the Styrofoam cup of tea from the tray and steeped the bag as she began to talk.

"Before continuing, I want you two to know something important. I know more about you than you think. You'll understand how this factors into everything soon enough." Sadie Cooper paused to take a drink of her tea.

"For example, Mr. Stiles, you graduated from a seminary but decided not to pursue a life in the priesthood. Not because of what you learned about the Vatican, but because you liked chasing the ladies too much. Nonetheless, you have been exposed to history and traditions others have not. After which, you immersed yourself in the profession of emergency management. You're an adrenaline junkie, Mr. Stiles, and proved that you know how to think on your feet. Finally, in 1981, you took the exam for the New York City Police Department and achieved the highest score on record, which still stands. You were disqualified, though, because of your eyesight."

"Gina, you also scored the highest in your police entrance exam, and graduated at the top of your class at the academy. Your performance reviews were the best on the force, and you were solicited by the FBI and other agencies. You declined due to family reasons, a move I suspect you have always regretted. Your career has always been second to your daughter."

"Okay, so you've done your homework on us," Gina snapped at the mention of her daughter. "Let's just stick to the case."

Sadie Cooper reached into her bag again, pulling out a third, thicker manila envelope. She handed it to me across the desk My name was clearly visible neatly printed across the front in black magic marker. The envelope was sealed and carefully taped shut.

"I've taken the liberty to type up everything you need to know about what's been going on in Lakewood over the last twenty years. Inside you will find documents, copies of newspaper clippings, and other material you'll need, should you decide to take up the daunting task of exposing a darkness so black, sins so horrendous, and a world that few know exists."

Mrs. Cooper continued. "But I have but one request, Mr. Stiles. Please don't open this packet until after I've left your office. In fact, I ask that you wait until sometime after 4:00 p.m. I am giving it to you now as a show of good faith, and that my intentions are honorable. I ask only that you will afford me the same goodwill by giving me this one simple courtesy. I think that after our discussion, you will be convinced of my sincerity and that my only intention is to help those who have been hurt by my late husband and his friends."

"How did you solve the murder of my uncle? How is it possible that you know that an arrest is imminent?"

"First of all, Marc, if I may call you Marc, I did not solve the murder, *you guys did.* Both of you, through your actions in Lakewood and in Florida. You pushed the proper buttons, put the pressure on, asked the right questions, and didn't back down when you had the chance. No one had the guts to do that, except for you two."

"I'm not sure it's guts, Mrs. Cooper, as much as ignorance and a genuine interest in justice," I interjected.

"Secondly, the police had to make an arrest now because they knew that you were making discoveries and connections that while they were not directly related to your uncle's murder, were exposing secrets and closets full of skeletons. And skeletons don't like to be confined to closets."

"Exactly what kind of secrets, Mrs. Cooper?"

"The kind that ruin reputations, marriages and careers. The kind that put people in prison. The kind that sentence people to hell, whether it's in this life or for all of eternity. It's all in the packet, Marc. You and Gina will find it informative. But I must warn you both, you will never look at certain things and people the same way ever again."

Just as Sadie Cooper brought the Styrofoam cup back up to her lips, the distant sound of sirens permeated the relative quiet of my office. I looked at Gina, who was staring a hole through Mrs. Cooper.

"A little early, I guess, but better too early than too late. Let's go over to the window and you'll see that everything I've said to you has been the truth."

We walked to the window overlooking the parking lot in front of our building which afforded us a view of the small plaza and diner across the street. We arrived at the window just in time to see one of the marked cruisers driving around to the rear of the plaza, while another marked cruiser stopped in front. The light bar on the top of the vehicle in front of the diner continued to flash, despite the absence of its driver.

Less than a minute later, Gina and I watched a middle-aged black male of slender build, his hands cuffed behind him, being escorted from the diner by two Lakewood Police officers, one who I immediately recognized as Jenkins. After they eased the man into the back of the patrol car, Jenkins looked up at my window and gave us a 'thumbs up.' It was Jenkins who escorted the prisoner from the diner.

"Do you believe me now, Marc?"

"For all we know, that could have been nothing more than a cheap parlor trick you set up in advance. That man might have nothing to do with my uncle's murder."

"I suppose you're right, Marc. Why don't you call the police station in a few minutes and ask Jenkins yourself. I'll be happy to wait with you until I'm proved correct. In the meantime, I'll do my best to answer all of your questions."

I didn't need to call the police station. The office telephone rang and Annie picked up the receiver. In the stillness of the office, we could hear Annie's footsteps as she walked toward my door and knocked. "Marc, Detective McCarty is on the phone, asking for you."

I lifted the handset from its cradle without taking my eyes off of Sadie Cooper.

"Mr. Stiles, this is Detective McCarty. I'm pleased to report that we made an arrest in the murder of your uncle just a few minutes ago. I wanted you to be the first to know. As a professional courtesy, I can give you a few minutes before I call your father in case you would like to alert him ahead of time."

"How do you know it's him?" I asked McCarty.

"We got an anonymous tip with his name and place of employment about a week ago, but nobody ever bothered to follow up until yesterday. Since he's been in the system before, we had his prints on file. We got a match on his prints this morning from the State Police Crime Lab.

"Who is he?"

"His name is Alan Macy Webber, originally from Columbus. He was in the system for a car-jacking and assault with a deadly weapon until his parole two weeks ago. It was a mix-up, a mess. I haven't quite figured out how he wasn't identified sooner, seeing that we had him in custody two days after your uncle's murder. He was downstate all that time. Then he came back here and got a job at the diner."

"And he was released?" I asked with more than a hint of anger. "Not just released, but working not more than a hundred yards from my office? Are you kidding me?" I began to raise my voice.

"Yeah, I'm upset too, Marc. This should have never happened. It was as if he was somehow invisible. Look, I'll talk to you later and fill you in on the rest of the details. Right now, I've got to get him back into the system."

"Some system," I said , not expecting a response.

I heard the noise of McCarty hanging up the telephone, then silence.

"Well, Marc?" Gina asked.

"It's him."

"Okay, Mrs. Cooper, so you've proved your legitimacy. Wanna fill us in?" I asked.

"I do. I just hope you're ready, Mr. Stiles. I hope you're ready, Ms. Russell."

CHAPTER 22

Uncomfortable Answers

"My husband was a government operative when he was first brought over from Germany as a budding Nazi. His resume is extensive in the area of mind control experiments. Programs that the government deny exist. Subjects that people mock as being conspiracy nonsense, but it's real. And Benjamin, I mean Rudolph, was a real part of it. In fact, he was active in this network of government operatives until his death.

"There are programs that exist right now, some led by monsters like Benjamin, that conduct mind control experiments on children. Unthinkable experiments. Children who have gone missing, runaways, and those who have gotten themselves into drugs and trouble. Those put into the system, never to be heard from again. And those who are just plain innocent victims, like my nephew, Lucas Manning." Sadie drank the remaining tea from her cup and opened the second one, and continued.

Gina sat up and looked directly at Sadie Cooper. "I have an interest in that case, Mrs. Cooper. I want to know what happened to him."

"My late husband would not tell me where he is, other than he's still alive. I'm hoping that the information in that envelope, Ms. Russell, will help him and other missing children."

Sadie Cooper continued. "I would stay myself to help, but I would not last one more day in Lakewood, or anywhere, for that matter, under my own name or otherwise out in the open. I would be arrested or killed, or both. It's the way the system works, but maybe you two can change that," Mrs. Cooper said, her eyes beginning to well up. "As best as I can tell, you two are the only ones who have a chance at blowing this dark brotherhood of the demonic wide open. And I'm not being melodramatic, either."

"Wait, are you saying that your life is in danger?" Gina asked.

"Not anymore, I'm already dead. My body won't be found for a few more hours, though."

"Oh, this is just too much. For crying out loud, Gina. Just what in the hell is going on here? Did we fall into some sort of bad episode of the Twilight Zone?" Gina held up her hand to quiet me.

"What do you mean, you're already dead?"

"They'll find my badly burned body in my car this afternoon. They will blame my death on a horrible accident, or maybe even suggest that I killed my husband and then myself. However, only *one* of those stories will be true. By then, I'll be on a plane to somewhere far from here, living a new life, thanks to someone buried deeply within the government with a soft heart for victims trapped in lives like mine. A 'white hat,' of sorts."

"How do you know that you can trust this knight in shining armor?"

"Because he's my brother. He loved Lucas and hated Benjamin. He saw what was going on inside the secret government programs, and has done his best to expose it. Much of the information you need to completely understand everything is inside that packet."

"How can you be so sure that you can trust us?" I asked. "I mean, we can call the police right now."

"You could, but you won't. At least I'm counting on you not to. And if you really think about it, given everything you've seen since taking on this case, who exactly can you trust, Marc?"

"She's got a point there, Marc."

"Tell me about my uncle and his murder."

"Your uncle was a victim, Marc, in many ways. He was nothing more than an experiment to the government, an experiment gone bad. He was exposed to trauma based mind control in the army, hideous things, at the hand of my husband, at least in part."

"But he was lost in the system during the chaos created by the Senate committee hearings back in the 1960's and 1970's. He became like a latent virus to his controllers. He began to unravel, became more careless, and began to recall some memories that should have been kept repressed, according to Benjamin. He had to be terminated, or else he could have exposed the whole program."

Sadie Cooper stopped briefly to collect her thoughts. "He was collecting photographs and evidence, not for blackmail or his own perverse delight, but to expose what was done to him and others. Given more time, he could have exposed many people in the government operation, including Houghton, Landers, and even Benjamin."

"He became exponentially more dangerous when Martin Tingsley began confiding in him about what he had gone through. My late husband, the man you know as Benjamin Cooper, was ordered to terminate them both, and erase all evidence that would associate any government program to them. That's when he ordered one of his 'disposables,' the man you know as Alan Macy Webber, to do the deed.

"Webber was given a special command, consisting of audible and visual cues, to kill your uncle. Those cues were given to him at the bookstore, and he followed them as programmed. The chances are good, better than good, in fact, that he has no memory of what happened."

"If that's the case, why so long of a wait to solve the murder. It seems to me that a quick arrest would have prevented us from getting involved," I asserted.

"Ah, as they say, even the best made plans go awry. Some things are just out of the control of others. Webber was supposed to be caught by the prints he left at the scene, and be dead before he could be put on trial, just in case his memory suddenly returned. The Lakewood cops screwed up by allowing him to sit in prison. He was supposed to be killed on the inside, but that did not go as planned. Then he was supposed to be shot in a drive-by shooting after his release, but that was screwed up. Benjamin was getting heat from his superiors, especially since you two suddenly emerged on the scene. Your high profile saved the both of you."

"So why is Webber still alive, then? Why arrest him, rather than kill him?

"That might have happened, except the man who would give that order took his own life just a few days ago, remember? No one saw that coming."

"If you knew all of these things, Mrs. Cooper, early on, why didn't you come to us right away. You could have saved us a lot of time and trouble, a lot of gas money, and a lot of grief. Why did you let us go to Florida, given what you already knew?" I asked.

"I had to know you could be trusted. I had to know you were willing to go the distance, to move mountains. I had to get a sense of your character. You can chalk it up to paying your dues, I suppose. Anyway, would you have believed me if you did not see some things for yourself in Florida?"

"Fair enough," I mumbled, as I rubbed the side of my head

"What about Martin Tingsley? Why is *he* still alive? Gina asked.

"Because Benjamin Cooper isn't."

"What about the photographs in my uncle's dresser? Did Webber take those?" I asked.

"No, but they did find their way into Benjamin's hands."

"How is that possible if the killer didn't take them? Blood transfer stains were found on the inside of the dresser drawer," I asked.

"Marc, there are still some things I don't know. That's one of them. I guess that will be up to you to determine, if you choose to do so."

"Where do we go from here, Mrs. Cooper?"

"The way I see it, you've got two choices. The murder of your uncle has been solved. Chances are good that no one will ever know the role you played in the capturing of his murderer. No one will ever know the world that you have partially uncovered, and the lives you have saved by your involvement. Trust me, there are many, but you will not know about them, at least not directly. You can continue to take your routine cases, as no one will be bothering your agency because of your involvement. The pressure will be off by the time I leave here."

Sadie Cooper's eyes met mine, turned to Gina's and then back to me as if she was looking for some sort of confirmation from each of us.

"Then again, you have another choice, Marc and Gina. You can choose to continue your investigation into an underworld that few know exists. A world of Satan worship, a world of satanic ritual abuse, a world where children disappear and people think they are doing their part by merely posting the kid's pictures on the sides of milk cartons. They are well intentioned, but are fools, ignorant to a reality as old as mankind itself that they don't know exists," said Mrs. Cooper.

"You can serve a higher master. You can choose to expose real evil, although be forewarned, the price is high as you will be mocked, ridiculed, and called crazy. The choice is yours. But before making it, may I suggest something?"

"What's that, Mrs. Cooper?" Gina asked.

"Pray about it."

"One more thing I'd like to give you, if I may. Perhaps a better way to say it is that I don't want this anywhere near me. It belonged to Benjamin. He wore it all of the time. He had it on him when I, er, I mean when he died."

Sadie Cooper reached into her bag and pulled out a plastic baggie and handed it to me. The first thing I noticed was the contents were very heavy, very dense for its size. I removed the item from the baggie and closely inspected it. Gina gasped at its sight. It was identical to the chain and adornment worn by her assailant in Florida.

The chain was gold, and the circle attached was very ornate, with the head of a goat inside of the circle. It was a Baphomet symbol. On the obverse, I noticed small etchings that included a .999 gold designation, along with the "SS" lightening symbol used by the Nazis.

"It's solid gold. It was made from the gold taken from Nazi concentration camps. The gold that's in this trinket was not from the jewelry of the Jews, but from their teeth. I thought you should know that."

Looking closer at it, there was something else I noticed. I looked at Gina, then at Sadie Cooper.

"It's stained by blood."

Epilogue

Sadie Cooper left our office as quietly as she entered. We did not press her for more information, nor did we violate her request that we wait until she was gone before opening the packet she left for us. Shortly after her departure, my father called our office to ask us if we heard the news about the arrest made by the Lakewood Police Department. "I guess we really didn't have to hire you and Paul. They finally got the killer!" he exclaimed.

"I guess they did, dad," was my simple response.

"I'm sorry if we wasted any of your time, Marc," he said.

"Think nothing of it. Glad it all worked out."

At 4:00 p.m., right on schedule, Sadie Cooper was in the air, and in investigative parlance, 'in the wind.' I have not seen or heard from her since, nor has Gina.

I suppose that's reasonable since her body, or that of a body that matched her description, was found at the bottom of the same ravine where Martin Tingsley's mother was found, at least according to a news report on the radio at the top of the hour news report broadcast at exactly 4:00 p.m.

At 4:15 p.m., we received notice from St. Elizabeth's Hospital that Roger Braun had died.

From 4:15 until 5:00 p.m., Annie, Gina and I packed up all of the index cards and took down the yarn from the cork boards. We marked each box and locked them in a closet. Annie hugged both of us before she left for the day, congratulating us for our hard work.

At 4:30 p.m., Gina was in my office when we opened the packet of information given to us by Sadie Cooper. We were stunned by its contents, and spent the next 5 hours pouring over everything inside. One thing was very clear. Neither one of us would ever look at the world, our government and their secret programs, or even those walking among us the same way ever again.

There's another thing that should be clear, especially in matters relating to true murder and conspiracy cases. They are hardly tidy, and many questions remain unanswered, despite the arrest and conviction of a man occupying a prison cell.

One thing Sadie Cooper did for us is to give us a head start on answering those question left unanswered within this writing.

The answers are out there, it's just a question of whether you *really* want to know them. For once you know them, you cannot "un-know" them. You cannot go back to a time of innocence.

What began as a cold-case investigation of my uncle's murder took an unexpected turn, opening an entirely different world to me personally and professionally. It is a world that consists of unthinkable and unspeakable evil and sinister forces of seduction working behind the scenes to influence people, including the most powerful and popular among us, from community leaders to entertainers. These forces of evil have the power to move not only people but entire nations, and they are exponentially increasing with each passing day.

These undercurrents of evil are pervasive and the deceptions used by these forces are many. Today, perhaps, you might only sense them. Soon, I suspect, you will see and perhaps experience them.

It took me a long time to understand that our fight is truly against the principalities, powers and the rulers of darkness in this world, against spiritual wickedness in high places as written in the Book of Ephesians of the Holy Bible. It is my sincere hope that your understanding will come much quicker, for time is short, and the battle is raging.

While the investigation into my uncle's murder is considered closed, the results of the larger investigation have yet to be unveiled.

ABOUT THE AUTHOR

Douglas J. Hagmann has been a licensed investigator in the private sector for the last 30 years. As a private detective, Hagmann has worked well over 5,000 cases and is recognized as a surveillance specialist. He has worked as an informational and operational asset for various federal and state law enforcement agencies.

Doug Hagmann now hosts a popular radio and video talk show each weeknight from 7:00-10:00 PM ET on the Global Star Radio Network and simulcast on YouTube and other venues.

He has four websites. The first two relate to his talk show and topical news items, and the third provides a platform for his own investigative research and analysis of current events. The fourth provides information specific to this book and items related to the topics addressed in *Stained By Blood.* In that order, they are:

www.HagmannandHagmann.com
www.HagmannReport.com
www.HomelandSecurityUS.com
www.StainedByBlood.com

36708102R00128

Made in the USA
San Bernardino, CA
30 July 2016